LEE 95

D1496948

NATIONAL ANTHEM

God save our gracious King,
Long live our noble King,
   God save the King.
Send him victorious,
Happy and glorious,
Long to reign over us,
   God save the King.

Thy choicest gifts in store,
On him be pleased to pour.
   Long may he reign!
May he defend our laws,
And ever give us cause
To sing with heart and voice,
   God save the King!

PATHWAYS TO READING—BOOK III

Golden Windows

ONTARIO

AUTHORIZED BY THE MINISTER OF EDUCATION
FOR ONTARIO

PRICE 20 CENTS

THE PRICE PRINTED ON THIS BOOK DOES NOT REPRESENT THE TOTAL
COST, AS AN ADDITIONAL SUM IS PAID TO THE PUBLISHER BY THE
DEPARTMENT OF EDUCATION

TORONTO
THOMAS NELSON & SONS, LIMITED
1944

ACKNOWLEDGMENTS

For kind permission to reprint certain copyright material grateful acknowledgment is hereby made as follows; to Joan Agnew for "The Crown"; to D. Appleton-Century Company Inc. for "The Little Elf-Man" by John Kendrick Bangs, from *The St. Nicholas Book of Verse*, and for "Cobwebs" from *Fifty Country Rhymes for Children* by E. L. M. King; to Marie Bayne for "In the Far North" and "The Man Who Did Not Like Music"; to Enid Blyton for "The Wonderful Sun"; to Jonathan Cape Limited and to the author for "Nature's Friend" from *Collected Poems of W. H. Davies*; to *Child Life* and to the authors for "Finding Fairies" by Marjorie Barrows, "Moon Song" by Mildred Plew Meigs, and "A Goblinade" by Florence Page Jacques; to Doubleday, Doran & Company, Inc., for "The Animal Store" and "General Store" from *Taxis and Toadstools* by Rachel Field, copyright 1926; to E. P. Dutton & Co., Inc., New York (by whom it is published and copyrighted) for "Kari the Elephant" taken from *Kari the Elephant* by Dhan Gopal Mukerji; to Eleanor Farjeon for "The Little Lady's Roses"; to Ginn & Company, Publishers, for "A Beautiful Ball" from *Seven Little Sisters* by Jane Andrews; to Harcourt, Brace and Company, Inc., for "The Procession" from *Little Girl and Boy Land* by Margaret Widdemer; to Oliver Herford for "The Elf and the Dormouse"; to Houghton Mifflin Company for "Parliament Hill" from *Songs out of School* by H. H. Bashford; to Little, Brown & Company and to the author for "The Golden Windows" by Laura E. Richards; to The Macmillan Company of Canada Limited, Toronto, for "The Fifteen Acres" by James Stephens; to The Macmillan Company, New York, and The Macmillan Company of Canada, Limited, Toronto, and to the author for "The First Easter Bunny" from *A Child's Book of Holiday Plays* by Frances Gillespy Wickes; to the *Manchester Guardian* and to the author for "Merriboy" by F. H. Finlayson; to Robert M. McBride and to the author for "Otherwise" from *The Coffee-Pot Face* by Aileen Fisher; to McClelland & Stewart Limited for "Spring Waking" and "Peterkin Spray" by Isabel Ecclestone Mackay and "A Child's Song of Christmas" by Marjorie L. C. Pickthall; to Thomas Nelson & Sons, Limited for "The Tar-Baby" by Joel Chandler Harris, retold by Enid Blyton, "A Market in Jamaica" by Marie Bayne, and "Little Orphan Robin" by Alice Wetherell; to Thomas Nelson & Sons, Limited and to the authors for "The Laughing Dragon" by Richard Wilson, "Popocatepetl" and "Latitude and Longitude" from *The Muse Amuses* by Hugh Chesterman, and "Mah Sing's Valentine" by Helen Dickson; to James B. Pinker & Son and to the author for "Full Moon" by Walter De la Mare; to *Punch*, reprinted by permission of the proprietors, and to the author for "A Fairy Went A-Marketing" from *Fairies and Chimneys* (London: Methuen & Co.) and "The Fairy Tailor" from *The Fairy Flute* (London: Methuen & Co.) by Rose Fyleman; to Scott, Foresman and Company for "My Chickadee Guests" by Ernest Harold Baynes from *The Elson Readers, Book Three*, copyright 1912, 1913, 1920, 1927; to Charles Scribner's Sons for "The Land of Story-Books" and "Foreign Children" by Robert Louis Stevenson, "The Duel" by Eugene Field, and "One, Two, Three" by Henry Cuyler Bunner; to Silver Burdett Company and to the author for "Flowers that Tell Time" by Kate Louise Brown; to Frederick A. Stokes Company (Canada) Limited for "Little Maid of Far Japan" by Annette Wynne; to the Viking Press, Inc., New York, for "The Woodpecker" from *Under the Tree* by Elizabeth Madox Roberts, copyright 1922 and 1930; to Lydia A. C. Ward for "Why?"; to Frances Shelley Wees for "Canada's Child"; to Frances Wright for "The Brook that Found the Sea."

Every reasonable care has been taken to trace ownership of copyright material. Information will be welcomed which will enable the publishers to rectify in subsequent editions any incorrect reference or credit.

PRINTED AND BOUND IN CANADA BY
W. J. GAGE & CO., LIMITED, TORONTO
1944

CONTENTS

CONTENTS

ONE, TWO, THREE

(See page 210)

FABLES & FAIRY-TALES

Some of the stories and poems in your book were first told thousands of years ago to boys and girls herding their sheep on the hill-sides. Others are new, just written for us who live now. If you like the stories and poems, you can find others in books in your library.

1. FINDING FAIRIES

When the winds of March are wakening
  The crocuses and crickets,
Did you ever find a fairy near
  Some budding little thickets,
Straightening her golden wings and
  Combing out her hair?
    She's there!

And when she sees you creeping up
  To get a closer peek,
She tumbles through the daffodils,
  Playing hide-and-seek,

9

And creeps into the tulips till
   You can't find where she's hid.
     Mine did!

Have you ever, ever come across
   A little toadstool elf
Reading by a firefly lamp
   And laughing to himself,
Or a saucy fairy queen upon
   Her favourite dragonfly?
     So've I!

It's fun to see a fairy flutter
   Off a catkin boat,
And wrap her fairy baby in
   A pussywillow coat;
Oh, don't you love the fairies
   And their fairy babies too?
     I do!

               —Marjorie Barrows.

MAKING MUSIC AND PICTURES FROM A POEM

One class read the poem together, and then they drew pictures of it.

To read the poem, the class chose four good readers. Each good reader read a verse, and when he came to the last two words, the whole class joined in. They read it so beautifully that it sounded like music.

Before the class drew their pictures, they read the poem carefully, and watched for the scenes to draw. They found eight. Are there more? Then the class divided itself into groups, and each group drew one of the pictures on a large piece of old wall-paper.

2. THE MAKER OF FLOWERS

O Sing and his wife lived happily in their small house and little garden. Near the house of O Sing lived old Wan and old Wan's wife. O Sing was good, and was kind to all his neighbours. Old Wan was not a kind man.

O Sing had a dog which he called Darr. One day he found Darr barking and digging at the foot of a tree. In the earth where Darr had been digging, there lay a pile of gold money.

Old Wan and his wife soon heard of the good fortune of their neighbours and came to call upon them.

"May we have your dog," said old Wan, "to come and live at our house for a while?"

O Sing said, "Take him, if he can be of use to you. He is a good dog. Be kind to him."

Wan and his wife took Darr home with them and led him into the garden. At the foot of a tree, they shoved Darr's nose into the ground and said "Now, dig."

Darr dug, and the black earth flew from his paws. But from the hole that he made, nothing came but the black earth.

Wan and his wife were angry. "You are a good-for-nothing dog," they cried. Then they beat Darr until he was dead, and buried him under the tree.

When O Sing heard what his neighbours had done, he begged them to sell him the wood of the tree.

Wan sold him the tree, and O Sing cut it down and took it home. From the wood of the tree O Sing and his wife made a tub, and in it they planted seeds. The next day the tub was full of plants bearing beautiful fruit. O Sing's wife picked the fruit and gave it to a poor family.

When old Wan and his wife heard of the wonderful tub, they came to call upon O Sing.

"May we borrow your tub?" they said.

"Take it," said O Sing, "if it can be of use to you."

Wan and his wife took the tub home and planted seeds in it. When the seeds did not grow, they were so angry that they put the tub in the fire.

When O Sing heard what his neighbours had done, he begged them to sell him the ashes of the tub.

Wan sold him the ashes, and O Sing took them home.   He scattered a few ashes in his garden.

Then a strange thing happened.   A cherry tree that had been dead began to grow beautiful flowers.

Everybody talked so much about the beautiful flowers that even the king heard about them. He sent for O Sing, and said, "My favourite cherry tree is dead.   Can you make it flower?"

O Sing scattered some of his ashes around the cherry tree, and the tree began to flower. Never before had there been such beautiful flowers upon the tree.

The king was so pleased that he called O Sing "The Maker of Flowers."

When Wan heard of O Sing's good fortune, he was very angry. He took some ashes from his kitchen fire and went through the streets crying, "Who wishes his trees to flower? I am the maker of many flowers."

The king called Wan to the palace, and said, "My next favourite cherry tree is dead. Can you make it flower?"

Wan threw some ashes around it, but it did not flower. He threw more and more ashes around the tree, but still it was dead. He emptied his basket of ashes upon the tree, and the wind blew the ashes into the king's eyes.

The king was so angry that he put Wan to work for the rest of his life, carrying ashes from the palace. But O Sing, the Maker of Flowers, lived happily with his wife in his small house and little garden.

—An Eastern Fable.

3. THE LITTLE ELF-MAN

I met a little Elf-man once,
    Down where the lilies blow.
I asked him why he was so small
    And why he didn't grow.

He slightly frowned, and with his eye
    He looked me through and through.
"I'm quite as big for me," said he,
    "As you are big for you."

—JOHN KENDRICK BANGS.

MAKING VERSES

Can you write a third verse for the poem? In a third verse, the elf might go on to say how small the man would look beside large animals. He might say,

> "Beside giraffes or elephants,
> "You'd not look tall, yourself . . ."

Try to write the next two lines of the verse.

---

4. THE ELF AND THE DORMOUSE

> "Elf-men, they say, sleep never a wink;
> But dormice are never awake, I think,"

wrote one boy when his teacher asked what a dormouse is.

Under a toadstool crept a wee Elf,
Out of the rain, to shelter himself.

Under the toadstool sound asleep,
Sat a big Dormouse all in a heap.

Trembled the wee Elf, frightened, and yet,
Fearing to fly away lest he get wet.

To the next shelter—maybe a mile!
Sudden the wee Elf smiled a wee smile.

Tugged till the toadstool toppled in two,
Holding it over him, gaily he flew.

Soon he was safe home, dry as could be.
Soon woke the Dormouse—"Good gracious me!

Where is my toadstool?" Loud he lamented,
—And that's how umbrellas first were invented.

—OLIVER HERFORD.

PICTURE CUT-OUTS

Make picture cut-outs for the poem. How many should you make?

The dormouse looking for his toadstool and the elf running away with it are two.

Can you think of another one?

---

5. THE TWO GOATS

Some fairy-tales are very old. This story about the goats was written more than 2000 years ago. Is it a fairy-tale? What kind of story is it?

One day two goats met on a ledge on the side of a high cliff. The ledge was so narrow that there was not room for them either to pass each other or to turn round and go back. A steep rock rose straight above them; a deep, dark hollow lay below!

What do you think the two goats did?

One of them, with great care, lay down on the narrow ledge, and pressed as close to

the rocky wall as he could. Then the other goat gently stepped over the body of his friend. As soon as he was past him, he ran safely on his way.

The goat that had lain down then drew himself up from his place. He also was safe and sound. He was now free to spring again from rock to rock, and to eat the sweet grass on the hills.

Two other goats left the valley, and climbed far up the mountain. After a time they met on the banks of a wild, rushing stream. A tree had fallen across the stream, and formed a bridge from one side to the other.

The goats looked at each other, and each wished to pass over first. They stood for a moment, each with one foot on the tree, thinking that the other goat would draw back. But neither of them did so, and they met at last in the middle of the narrow bridge.

They began to push and fight with their horns, till at last their feet slipped. Both fell into the swift stream, and were drowned.

—*From Æsop's Fables.*

MAKING A PICTURE STORY-BOOK

There are many more of Aesop's fables. The boys and girls of one class set out to look for them. They found ten that they liked. The class formed groups, and each group chose one of the stories and made a picture for it. All groups used sheets of paper of the same size. The best writer in each group wrote the story on another sheet of paper, also of the same size.

When pictures and stories were finished, the boys and girls bound their book and lent it to another class. The other class wrote a letter, thanking them for the beautiful book.

6. THE TRAVELLING MUSICIANS

If the farmyard animals were to make a band, and if the band started suddenly to play in the middle of the night, would the "music" frighten you? Perhaps you would think you had forgotten to turn off the radio! In this story the farmyard animals did make a band, and what excitement they caused!

A donkey who was too old to work heard his master say that he must be sold to the boneman.

"I will not stay here to be sold," thought the donkey. "I shall go to the city and play in the band."

He had not gone far when he saw a dog lying on the ground.

"Why do you lie there?" he asked.

"Oh," said the dog, "I am too old to help my master. He says that I must be sold to the boneman, so I have run away."

"Then come with me," said the donkey. "I am going to the city to play in the band. I can blow the horn, and you can tap the drum."

"Very well," said the dog; and off they went together.

They soon came to a cat sitting by the road and looking very sad.

"Why are you sad?" asked the donkey.

"How can I be happy?" said the cat. "I am too old to catch mice, and my mistress says that she must give me to the boneman, so I have run away."

"Come with us to the city," said the donkey. "You are a good night singer, so you can sing in our band."

"With all my heart," said the cat, and off they all went together.

After a while they came to a farmyard. A rooster stood on the gate, crowing and screaming with might and main.

"Why are you making so much noise?" asked the donkey.

"I shall tell you," said he. "The cook says that the guests are coming to-morrow, so she is going to make broth of me for their dinner."

"Listen," said the donkey. "You have a good voice. Come with us to the city to join the band."

"Thank you," said the rooster, and they all went on together.

At night they came to a forest.

"Let us stay here," said the donkey, and he lay down on the ground. The dog lay down, too.

The rooster perched near the top of a tree, and the cat found a place on one of its big branches.

Before they went to sleep the rooster saw a light in the forest. He called to his friends and told them what he saw.

"It must come from a house," said the donkey. "Let us go on and see."

"Yes," said the dog. "I should like a good bone for my supper."

When they reached the house, they saw that the light came from a very high window.

"How can we see into the room?" said the cat.

"I am not tall enough," said the dog.

"Nor I," said the donkey.

At last they thought of a plan. The donkey stood under the window, and the dog stood on his back. The cat climbed to the dog's back, and the rooster flew up on the cat's back.

"What do you see?" asked the donkey.

"What do I see?" said the rooster. "I see four robbers eating at a table. They have bread and meat and many other good things."

"That ought to be our supper," said the dog.

"Yes, yes!" cried the cat. "I am so hungry that I cannot sleep."

"We must drive the robbers away," whispered the rooster.   "But how can it be done?"

Then the four friends tried and tried to think of a plan.

At last the donkey said: "I know how we can frighten the robbers.   When I count three, let us all begin to make as much noise as we can. Now!—One! two! three!"

What a noise they made! The donkey brayed, and the dog barked, and the cat mewed, and the rooster crowed.

The robbers jumped up from the table and ran into the woods as fast as they could go.

Then the four friends went into the house and helped themselves to the food.

When they had eaten their supper, they put out the light, and each found a place to sleep. The donkey lay down in the yard. The dog went behind the door. The cat curled up in front of the fire, and the rooster flew to the back of a chair.

After some time the robbers, who had not fled far, got over their fright. One, bolder than the rest, entered the house. All was still and dark.

He took a candle from his pocket to light it at the coals on the hearth. But these coals were the two bright eyes of the cat. The cat did not like him to put the candle in her eye, so she sprang at his face and scratched him.

He ran to the door, and, as he was going out, the dog jumped up and bit his leg. On he ran through the yard, but the donkey wheeled round and kicked him on the back. The noise awoke the rooster, and he crowed with all his might.

The robber hurried to his comrades as fast as he could go. He told them that a witch was in the house, and had nearly scratched his eyes out; that a man with a knife had stabbed him in the leg; that a huge monster in the yard had hit him with a club; and that someone on the roof was telling them where he was. The robbers never dared to go back to that house.

The travelling musicians said that they would rather stay there than go on to the city, and for all I know they are still living in the little house in the woods.

—Jacob and Wilhelm Grimm.

Making a Moving Picture

This is a good story to make into a moving picture. Draw the pictures on a long roll of wall-paper. Wind the roll on a sawed-off broomstick, and by using another broomstick unwind it from one and wind it on the other at the same time. Show the pictures through a hole in a large cardboard box.

---

7. A GOBLINADE

A *goblinade* is just "a story about a goblin."

A green hobgoblin,
    Small but quick,
Went out walking
    With a black thorn stick.

He was full of mischief,
  Full of glee.
He frightened all
  That he could see.

He saw a little maiden
  In a wood.
He looked as fierce as
  A goblin should.
He crept by the hedge row,
  He said, "Boo!"
"Boo!" laughed the little girl,
  "How are you?"
"What!" said the goblin,
  "Aren't you afraid?"
"I think you're funny,"
  Said the maid.
"Ha!" said the goblin,
  Sitting down flat.
"You think I'm funny?
  I don't like that.
I'm very frightening.
  You should flee!"
"You're cunning," she said,
  "As you can be!"
Then she laughed again, and

Went away.
But the goblin stood there
    All that day.

A beetle came by, and
    "Well?" it said.
But the goblin only
    Shook his head.
"For I am funny,"
    He said to it.
"I thought I was alarming,
    And I'm not a bit.
If I'm amusing,"
    He said to himself,
"I won't be a goblin,
    I'll be an elf!
For a goblin must be goblin
    All the day,
But an elf need only
    Dance and play."

So the little green goblin
    Became an elf.
And he dances all day, and
    He likes himself.

—FLORENCE PAGE JACQUES.

8. THE GOLDEN FISH

The children in Russia are fond of this story about a greedy old woman who learned her sad lesson.

Long ago, an old man and his wife lived upon an island in the middle of the sea. They were so poor that they were often without food.

One day the man had been fishing for many hours, but without any success. At last he caught a small golden fish, with eyes as bright as diamonds.

"Put me back into the sea, kind man," cried the little fish. "I am so small that I would not make a meal for you."

The old man felt so sorry for the little fish that he threw him back into the sea. As the golden fish swam away, he called out, "If ever you need anything, call on me. I shall come at once to help you. I shall do this because you were kind to me."

The fisherman laughed, because he did not believe that a fish could help him. When he went home, he told his wife about the wonderful fish he had caught.

"What!" she cried. "You put him back

into the sea after you had caught him? How
foolish you were! We have no food in the
house, and now, I suppose, we must starve!"

She scolded him so much that at last the
poor man went back to the sea. He did not
really believe that the fish could help him,
but he thought it would do no harm to find
out whether he could. "Golden fish, golden
fish!" he called. "Come to me, I pray."

As the last word was spoken, the wonderful
fish popped his head out of the water.

"I have kept my promise, you see," said
the fish. "What can I do for you, my good
friend?"

"There is no food in the house," answered
the old man, "and my wife is very angry with
me for putting you back into the sea."

"Do not be troubled," said the golden fish.
"Go home. You will find food, and to spare."

The old man hurried home as fast as he
could go to see if his little friend had spoken
the truth. He found the oven full of fine
white loaves of bread!

"I did not do so badly for you, after all,
good wife," said the fisherman, as they ate
their supper.

But his wife was not satisfied yet. The more she had, the more she wanted. All that night she lay awake, planning other things to ask of the golden fish.

"Wake up, you lazy man!" she cried to her husband, early the next morning. "Go down to the sea and tell your fish that I must have a new wash-tub!"

The old man did as his wife bade him. The moment he called, the fish came, and seemed quite willing to do as he was asked. When the fisherman returned to his home, he saw in the kitchen a new wash-tub!

"Why didn't you ask for a new house, too?" his wife asked angrily. "If you had asked for a fine house, he would have given it to us. Go back and say that we must have a new house."

The fisherman did not like to trouble his friend again so soon; but when he went to the water, he found the golden fish as willing to help him as before.

"Very well," said the fish. "A new house you shall have." When the old man went back to his wife, he found her living in a beautiful house instead of his little hut!

It would have pleased him greatly if his wife had now been contented. But she was a foolish woman, and even yet she was not satisfied. "Tell your golden fish," she said the next morning, "that I want to live in a palace. I want a great many servants to wait upon me, and a splendid carriage to ride in."

Once more her wish was granted. After this, the poor fisherman's life was even more unhappy than before; for his wife would not allow him to share her palace, but made him live in the stable.

"At any rate," he said to himself, "I have peace here." But before long she sent for him again.

"Go down to the sea, and call the golden

fish," she commanded. "Tell him I wish to be Queen of the Waters and to rule over all the fishes in the sea."

The poor old man thought that he would be sorry for the fishes if she ever ruled over them; for riches had quite spoiled her. Still, he did not dare to disobey her, so once more he called his good little friend.

When the golden fish heard what the fisherman's wife wanted this time, he cried out, "Make your wife Queen of the Waters! Never! She is not fit to rule others, for she cannot rule herself. Go home! You shall see me no more!"

The old man went sorrowfully home, and found the palace changed to a hut. His wife was no longer dressed in rich garments; she was wearing the simple dress of a fisherman's wife. But she was now quiet and mild, and much easier to live with than she had been before.

"After all," thought the fisherman, "I am not sorry that the palace became a hut again."

He worked hard to make a living for himself and his wife, and somehow his hooks

were never empty, so that the old couple
always had food. Sometimes when he drew in
a fish, the sun would gleam brightly upon its
scales. Then the old man would think of his
little friend who had been so kind to him. But
he never saw the golden fish again.

—A Russian Tale.

Telling Stories

"I know a story like that," said one boy. "It's called
'The Woodman's Axe,' and it's about a woodman who let
his axe fall into the river." He told his story to the class.

Some of the other children found old tales to tell. They
called their story hour "A Story Festival."

---

9. A FAIRY WENT A-MARKETING

Elves are mischievous, goblins are fierce, but fairies are
nearly always kind.

A fairy went a-marketing—
    She bought a little fish;
She put it in a crystal bowl
    Upon a golden dish.
An hour she sat in wonderment
    And watched its silver gleam,
And then she gently took it up
    And slipped it in a stream.

A fairy went a-marketing—
   She bought a coloured bird;
It sang the sweetest, shrillest song
   That ever she had heard.
She sat beside its painted cage
   And listened half the day,
And then she opened wide the door
   And let it fly away.

A fairy went a-marketing—
   She bought a winter gown
All stitched about with gossamer
   And lined with thistledown.
She wore it all the afternoon
   With prancing and delight,
Then gave it to a little frog
   To keep him warm at night.

A fairy went a-marketing—
   She bought a gentle mouse
To take her tiny messages,
   To keep her tiny house.
All day she kept its busy feet
   Pit-patting to and fro,
And then she kissed its silken ears,
   Thanked it, and let it go.

            —Rose Fyleman.

10. THE FAIRY TAILOR

Do you remember our little fairy who "bought a winter gown, all stitched about with gossamer and lined with thistledown"? The following poem is about the fairy tailor who makes the fairies' clothes.

It has a song in it. As you read it, try to think of a tune to which you could sing the song.

Sitting on the flower-bed, beneath the hollyhocks,
I spied the tiny tailor who makes the fairies'
    frocks;
There he sat a-stitching all the afternoon,
And sang a little ditty to a quaint wee tune:
    "Gray for the goblins, blue for the elves,
      Brown for the little gnomes that live by
        themselves,
      White for the pixies that dance on the
        green—
      But where shall I find me a robe for the
        Queen?"

All about the garden his little men he sent,
Up and down and in and out unceasingly they
    went.
Here they stole a blossom, there they pulled a leaf,
And bound them up with gossamer into a glow-
    ing sheaf.

Petals of the pansy for little velvet shoon,
Silk of the poppy for a dance beneath the
moon,
Lawn of the jessamine, damask of the rose,
To make their pretty kirtles and airy fur-
belows.

Never roving pirates back from Southern Seas
Brought a store of treasures home more beautiful
than these.
They heaped them all about him in a sweet, gay
pile,
But still he kept a-stitching and a-singing all the
while:
"Gray for the goblins, blue for the elves,
Brown for the little gnomes that live by
themselves,
White for the pixies that dance on the
green,
But who shall make a royal gown to deck
the Fairy Queen?"

—ROSE FYLEMAN.

SINGING A SONG

If you cannot think of "a quaint wee tune" for the
ditty, look through your music books, and see if you can
find one. Try to sing it as gaily as the fairy tailor did.

11. OTHERWISE

There must be magic,
   Otherwise,
How could day turn to night?

And how could sailboats,
   Otherwise,
Go sailing out of sight?

And how could peanuts,
   Otherwise,
Be covered up so tight?

—AILEEN FISHER.

---

12. THE SLEEPING BEAUTY

The story of "The Sleeping Beauty" is one that the fathers and mothers of France used to tell their children long, long ago.

For your Reader, the story has been turned into a play that you may act.

Characters:

KING, QUEEN, PRINCESS, PRINCE, SEVEN FAIRIES, OLD FAIRY, YOUNG FAIRY, OLD WOMAN, FIRST OLD MAN, SECOND OLD MAN.

Scene I

A room in a king's palace. The King on his throne, with his lords and ladies near him. Enter to them the Queen with a baby in her arms.

KING. Here comes our royal daughter. (*Steps down from his throne to meet the Queen.*)

QUEEN. She is just six weeks old to-day, Your Majesty. See what a lovely child!

KING (*stooping to kiss the Princess*). Let the feast be made. I hope that the fairies will come with their gifts. Were they all asked to come?

QUEEN. Seven of them were invited. See, my lord, they come.

(*Seven fairies trip into the room and form a circle round the King, Queen, and Princess. They all look with shining eyes at the baby.*)

FIRST FAIRY. A gift, a gift! I give her beauty such as no maiden has ever had before.

SECOND FAIRY. A gift, a gift! I give her goodness. She shall be as good as she will be lovely to behold.

THIRD FAIRY. A gift, a gift! I give her hope. Even in trouble her face shall still be bright.

FOURTH FAIRY. A gift, a gift! I give her love of music. When she shall play the harp, the birds will be silent to listen.

FIFTH FAIRY. A gift, a gift! I give her love of animals. Even the wild things of the wood shall come at her call.

SIXTH FAIRY. A gift, a gift! I give her love of the open air, the woods and fields, the green hills, and the sunny sky.

SEVENTH FAIRY. I give her love. She shall love a handsome prince, and be dearly loved by him in return.

(*Enter an old fairy with white hair, carrying a wand in her hand. The King and Queen look at her with troubled faces.*)

OLD FAIRY. Oh ho! So you forgot all about me? You thought that I was dead, because I have been shut up in the tower for so long. But I shall pay you out for forgetting me. When the Princess is fifteen years old, she shall prick her finger with a spindle, and shall die of the wound.

(*The King looks very sad. The Queen and all her ladies begin to cry. All at once another fairy, very young and lovely, comes out from behind a curtain and trips forward.*)

YOUNG FAIRY. O King and Queen, do not be sad at heart. I cannot prevent your child from pricking her finger with a spindle, but she shall not die. She shall only sleep for a hundred years. And at the end of that time a king's son shall come and waken her with a kiss.

KING (*to one of his lords*). Send soldiers into every house in the land to destroy the spinning wheels. (*Turns to another lord.*) Let it be made known to all that anyone who is found with a spindle shall be put to death.

Scene II

A dark room in a high tower of the palace. A very old woman sits in a corner, spinning at a wheel. She never goes out, and so has not heard of the King's orders about spinning wheels and spindles. The Princess, now a lovely girl of fifteen, opens the door and looks in.

PRINCESS. What are you doing there, Goody?

OLD WOMAN. I am spinning, my pretty child. Won't you come in and watch?

(The Princess comes forward and stands by her side.)

PRINCESS. Oh, how clever you are! How quickly the wheel goes round! How cleverly you spin the wool into yarn! Let me try, please, Goody.

OLD WOMAN. You shall; but be careful. The spindle is sharp and may prick your finger.

PRINCESS. Oh, I'll be very careful. I'll sit down here. See how the wheel goes round! I take the wool in the fingers of my left hand like this. Now give me the spindle. *(She takes the spindle, but handles it in such a clumsy way that it pricks her finger.*)   Oh dear! Oh dear! I have pricked my finger! (*She falls down on the floor, and is soon in a deep sleep.*)

OLD WOMAN (*going to the door of her room*).   Help! Help! The Princess has fainted!

(*Maids and pages come running up. They try to waken the Princess, but cannot do so. Then they carry her away and lay her gently on her bed. At this moment the Young Fairy enters.*)

YOUNG FAIRY. No power on earth can wake her till a hundred years have passed. But I have a plan. I shall put all in the castle to sleep for a hundred years. And when the Princess wakes, you will be with her again. (*She waves her wand, and all go to sleep where they are.*)   Now I must pass through the palace. All shall sleep; the King and the Queen upon their thrones; the lords and the ladies in the chambers; the soldiers at the gate and on the walls; the cook and the maids in the kitchen; the flies on the walls and the spiders in the webs.

Scene III

A hundred years later. A country road by the side of a thick wood. Two old men in smock-frocks go slowly by.

First Old Man (*stopping to rest with his hands upon the top of his stick*). Ay, ay! Do you see this thick wood?

Second Old Man. Yes, friend. But why do you ask? It is only a wood like any other wood. But who comes here? The young Prince from the city over the mountains, I do declare. I know him by his rich clothes and the long sword by his side.

(*A handsome young man comes from the wood into the roadway, followed by two large hunting-dogs. The old men take off their hats and bow low before him.*)

Prince. Good-morrow, friends. Do you know anything of a castle in this wood?

First Old Man. And it may please Your Highness, fifty years ago I heard my father say that his father had told him there was a castle in the wood.

Prince. That must have been about a hundred years ago.

FIRST OLD MAN. I have not been to school and cannot reckon. What Your Highness says must be true.

PRINCE. What more did your father tell you?

FIRST OLD MAN. He said that in this castle a lovely princess and all her lords and ladies and servants lay sleeping.

PRINCE. Sleeping for a hundred years!

FIRST OLD MAN. Yes, indeed. And that the Princess would be wakened by the son of a king, who would cut his way through the wood with his sword.

PRINCE (*turning away toward the wood*). I go to set the lovely Princess free.

SCENE IV

A room in the palace. The Princess lies asleep upon the bed. The maids and pages sit or lie asleep in various parts of the room. The Prince enters with a drawn sword in his hand.

PRINCE. What a wonderful adventure! The King and Queen asleep upon their thrones! Servants and soldiers asleep in all parts of the castle! Dogs and horses asleep in the stables! And, at last, the lovely Princess! (*He steps lightly up to the bed, and looks down in wonder at the sleeping girl.*) How beautiful! She might have fallen asleep only yesterday! (*Kisses her.*)

PRINCESS (*opening her eyes*). Is it you, my Prince? I have waited for a long, long time.

PRINCE (*going down upon one knee*). My Princess! My bride!

(*Enter the Young Fairy with her wand in her hand and a bright smile upon her face.*)

YOUNG FAIRY. All is well! How I laughed to see the people wake up! No one seemed surprised. The King spoke to the Queen as if he had only taken a nap after dinner. The horses shook themselves, and the dogs barked. The pigeons took their heads from under their wings, and flew down from the roof into the fields. The flies on the wall began to buzz again. The spiders awoke and lay in wait for them. The fire in the kitchen blazed up. Round went the spit with the goose for the King's dinner on it. The maid went on plucking a fowl. And the cook gave the kitchen boy a box on the ear for having fallen asleep at his work.

PRINCE (*joining hands with the Princess*). Come, let us find the King and Queen, and ask their consent to our wedding.

(*They go out together, hand in hand.*)

—AN OLD FOLK-TALE.

DRESSING UP

"The Sleeping Beauty" is a play for which you may make costumes. Make dresses for the people; tissue-paper is a good thing to use. Make a spinning wheel, swords, sceptres, and crowns out of cardboard, and cover them with paper of different colours. Can you think of anything else that you could make?

If you do this play well, perhaps your teacher will let you invite your mothers to come and see you play it.

13. POOR MOON

One fine evening a traveller came to a village, but found none of the people at home. Later he found them gathered around a pond outside the village. They had brooms, rakes, and pitch-forks, and were reaching and reaching into the pond. Something seemed to have fallen into the water, and everyone was doing his best to pull it out.

"Hello!" cried the traveller, "what's the matter?"

"Matter enough!" cried the villagers; "the moon has fallen from the sky and has dropped into the pond, and we are trying to pull her out."

"Nonsense!" said the traveller, laughing. "Look up at the sky; there is the moon shining brightly as ever."

But the people turned angrily on the traveller with their brooms, rakes, and pitch-forks and drove him away.

"What nonsense the man talks," said they. "You have only to look down to see that the moon is in the water."

—An English Folk-Tale.

OUT OF DOORS

In this part of your Reader you will find poems and stories about the great out-of-doors. Some of you will like this part best, because it tells you of wonderful things you can see all about you and of interesting things you can do at your own homes.

1. A BEAUTIFUL BALL

The first story is about the big earth itself.

I have heard of a wonderful ball which floats in the sweet blue air, and has soft white clouds about it as it floats along.

There are many charming things to be told about this wonderful ball. Some of them you shall hear.

It is so large that many houses are built upon it. Men and women live upon it, and little children can play upon its surface.

In some places it is soft and green, like the
long meadows between the hills. In other
parts there are trees for miles and miles on
every side. All kinds of wild animals live
in the great forests that grow on this wonderful ball.

Then, again, in some places it is steep and
rough. And there are mountains so high
that the snow lies upon their tops all the year
round.

In other parts there are no hills at all, but
level land, and quiet little ponds of blue
water. There the white water-lilies grow, and
fishes play among the lily stems.

Now if we look on another side of the ball,
we shall see no ponds, but something very
dreary. A great plain of sand stretches
away on every side. There are no trees here,
and the sunshine beats down upon the burning sand.

We look again, and we see a great stretch
of water. Many islands are in the sea, and
great ships sail upon it.

Look at one more side of this ball as it
turns around. Jack Frost must have spent
all his longest winter nights here. For see

what a palace of ice he has built for himself.

How cold it looks! See the clear, blue ice, almost as blue as the sky. And look at the snow, drifts upon drifts, and the feathery flakes filling the air.

Now, what do you think of this ball, so white and cold, so warm and green, so dreary and rough, as it floats along in the blue air, with the pillows of white clouds about it? If you borrow the older children's geography books, you can find pictures of the high mountains, the hot deserts, the wide plains, and the meadows where the lilies blow.

—*Adapted from* JANE ANDREWS.

2. FULL MOON

Dick and the moon looked at each other—just looked. Each of them was so silent and so serious! Have you and the moon ever gazed at each other that way? Or does she always seem to smile, and wink at *you*?

One night as Dick lay half asleep,
    Into his drowsy eyes
A great still light began to creep
    From out the silent skies.
It was the lovely moon's, for when
    He raised his dreamy head,
Her surge of silver filled the pane
    And streamed across his bed.
So, for awhile, each gazed at each —
    Dick, and the solemn moon—
Till, climbing slowly on her way,
    She vanished and was gone.

—WALTER DE LA MARE.

MOON FACES

From a calendar find out when you may see the next new moon, the first quarter, the full moon, and the last quarter. Draw the moons, and write under each the date on which it may be seen. When the date comes, put a face on each moon to show the kind of weather on that date. How shall you draw a sunny face? a cloudy face? a rainy one?

3. THE WONDERFUL SUN

As Dick gazed silently at the moon, perhaps he thought about the Bible verse that says: "And God made two great lights; the greater light to rule the day, and the lesser light to rule the night: he made the stars also."—*Genesis 1:16*.

I have a watch on my wrist to tell me the time. At home you have a clock on your mantelpiece, and at school a big clock hangs on the wall ticking away the hours.

But there is a much bigger clock in the sky, and that is the wonderful sun. Every morning the sun rises and tells us it is day once more. Every evening it sets, and we know that night has come. The sun clock is never fast and never slow, but always exactly right.

At noon the sun is at its highest point in the sky, and our shadows are at their shortest. In the morning when the sun's rays slant through the trees, our shadows are long. And in the evening when the sun is setting and lighting up the sky with brilliant colours, our shadows are long again. Have you noticed that?

We love the sun because it gives us light and warmth. Even in winter-time we are glad to feel its rays, and to see the world brighten in the pale sunshine. In spring it makes the plants send up new leaves again. It melts the sparkling ice on the rivers and ponds. It wakes up the frogs and the toads. It makes us shout for joy. In summer we grow brown and healthy, and the sun gives us the strength we need for the dark, cold winter.

The sun is so bright that we cannot look at it without hurting our eyes. It is a great ball of fire, thousands of times as big as our earth. It is always shining, even when we cannot see it because of the clouds that hide it.

If we could go up in an aeroplane and pass right through the clouds, we should see that the sun is shining on them. Look for the silver rim of the clouds on a sunny day, when they pass in front of the sun; or, if it is evening, look for the golden rim. That will tell you that the sun is shining as brightly as ever, even though we cannot see it.

The sun always rises in the eastern sky, climbs in an arch, and sinks in the west. Although its light is gone from us, it is still shining for other boys and girls in far-away lands. When we are sleeping on our side of the round world, because the night is here, other children are waking because it is daylight, and the sun is shining for them.

The sun is a kind of doctor. It sends its rays into dark, unhealthy corners and cleanses them. Open your windows wide, and let the sunshine pour into your rooms. If anyone is feeling sad or ill, the sun will soon make him feel better.

If we had no sun to warm us, we should have no rain to make things grow. All day long the sun is causing moisture to rise from seas, rivers, ponds, and puddles. The moisture collects into dark clouds, and we look up at them and say, "It is going to rain." Then down comes a shower that waters our garden

for us, makes the crops grow in the fields, and
the grass in the meadows.

Did you know that the sun gave us our
moonlight? That sounds very strange, does
it not? The moon has no light of its own,
but is rather like a mirror throwing back the
light of the sun, which is shining on it from
the other side of the earth. The full moon
is so bright that by its light we can see to
walk down the streets at night. But moonlight is cold and silvery, not warm and golden
like the sunlight.

—ENID BLYTON.

A SUN-CLOCK

A teacher told his class how to make a sun-clock, and
said it was really called a sun-dial. He said that for thousands of years sun-dials were used to tell time.

The children thought they would like to make one.
They took a flower-pot full of earth, set it in a sunny window, and stood a pencil in the centre of it. At noon, they
made a mark on the edge of the pot where the shadow fell.

When the children had marked twelve o'clock, they
went on using the school clock to help them mark the
places where the shadows fell at one, two, three, and four.
And the next day they marked the morning hours.

What is funny about the story of a boy, long ago, who
took a lantern one night and went out to the sun-dial to
find out the time?

4. WHEN THE LITTLE BOY RAN AWAY

Nature is beautiful: the great earth, the sun, the moon, and the wind. But the little boy who ran away thought that sometimes the in-doors is better than the out-doors.

When the little boy ran away from home,
　The birds in the tree-tops knew,
And they all sang: "Stay!"
But he wandered away
　Under the skies of blue.
And the wind came whispering from the tree:
　"Follow me—follow me!"
And it sang him a song that was soft and sweet,
And scattered the roses before his feet
　That day—that day
　When the little boy ran away.

The violet whispered: "Your eyes are blue
　And lovely and bright to see;
And so are mine, and I'm kin to you,
　So dwell in the light with me!"
But the little boy laughed, while the wind in glee
Said: "Follow me—follow me!"
And the wind called clouds from their home
　in the skies,
And said to the violet: "Shut your eyes!"

That day—that day
When the little boy ran away.

Then the wind played leap-frog over the hills
 And twisted each leaf and limb;
And all the rivers and all the rills
 Were foaming mad with him;
And it was dark as darkest night could be,
But still came the wind's voice: "Follow me!"
And over the mountain and up from the hollow
Came echoing voices with "Follow him, fol-
  low!"
 That awful day
 When the little boy ran away.

Then the little boy cried: "Let me go—let me
  go!"
 For a scared, scared boy was he!
But the thunder growled from the black cloud:
  "No!"
 And the wind roared: "Follow me!"
And an old gray owl from a tree-top flew,
Saying: "Who are you-oo? who are you-oo?"
And the little boy sobbed: "I'm lost away,
And I want to go home where my parents stay!"

Oh! the awful day
When the little boy ran away.

Then the moon looked out from the cloud and
      said:
   "Are you sorry you ran away?
If I light you home to your trundle bed,
   Will you stay, little boy, will you stay?"
And the little boy promised—and cried and
      cried—
He would never leave his mother's side;
And the moonlight led him over the plain,
And his mother welcomed him home again.
   But oh! what a day
   When the little boy ran away!

—Author Unknown.

Reading Together

When people sing together, they make a choir. For
this poem, boys and girls may make a reading choir.

Choose a "choir leader" to help you keep together.

Read the first part softly, keeping your voices low.
Be sure to read it clearly.

At what verse do you think you should raise your
voices? How should you read the owl's cry?

When you have finished reading the poem together,
perhaps the choir leader would like to add, "East, West,
Home is best."

5. WINGS

In this story, Bobbie learned a secret that the warm earth usually keeps to itself.

Bobbie had six big white beans in a box. They were fine playthings, but one day he broke one of them in two.

"Oh, Mother," he cried, "I've broken one of my big white beans."

"Let me have it," said his mother, "and I'll tell you a lovely secret about it."

"A secret about a bean!" cried Bobby. "What is it, Mother?"

"Look!" his mother said, as she took the broken bean from him. "Can you see these tiny wings? They've been folded away in the heart of the bean for a long time. Now that it is broken, they can come out."

Bobby looked at the dainty wings and felt them. "Why do beans have wings?" he asked. "They don't fly, do they?"

"I'll show you," said his mother, and she put the bean into a glass of water. "To-morrow we'll look at it again, and see what has happened to the wings."

Next morning when they looked at the bean, they saw that the two little wings were

unfolding, and were turning a pretty soft green colour.

"That is what happens when beans are planted in the earth," said Mother. "Their little wings grow larger."

"Oh, then, let us plant the other five beans," begged Bobby.

So he dug five little holes in the soft earth of the garden, placed a big white bean in each hole, and over each he sprinkled a handful of fine black soil. After a few days, there were five pairs of little wings spreading themselves above the ground. On each stem, just below the little wings, Bobbie saw a large white bean broken in two in the middle.

"Oh, Mother," he cried, "here are the little wings! But, Mother," he added, "the beautiful big white beans are all spoiled. Each one is broken in two. Are they dead?"

"Yes," said his mother. "The big white bean must die so that the little white wings can get free to grow. If the big white bean did not break in two, the little wings would have to stay folded tightly in their little dark prison house. They could never push their way out and up into the sunlight."

Bobbie listened thoughtfully while his mother was speaking.

"That is wonderful, Mother," he said.

"Yes, my dear, it is wonderful," his mother answered. "It is God's way, and all His ways are wonderful."

—Lilith Shell.

Thinking about the Story

Copy each sentence, choosing for the blank space one of the words given:

1. Bobbie was very ...... (naughty, curious, beautiful).

2. Inside the bean, the wings are ...... (folded, lovely, broken).

3. The mother told Bobbie a ...... (fable, fairy-tale, secret).

4. Bobbie listened ...... (breathlessly, thoughtfully, patiently).

5. When the wings grow, the mother bean .... (grows too, dies, disappears).

6. God's ways are always ...... (pleasant, difficult, wonderful).

6. SPRING WAKING

A Snowdrop lay in the sweet, dark ground.
  "Come out," said the Sun, "come out!"
But she lay quite still, and she heard no sound;
  "Asleep!" said the Sun, "no doubt!"

The Snowdrop heard, for she raised her head,
  "Look spry," said the Sun, "look spry!"
"It's warm," said the Snowdrop, "here in bed."
  "O fie!" said the Sun, "O fie!"

"You call too soon, Mr. Sun, *you do*!"
  "No, no," said the Sun, "Oh, *no*!"
"There's something above, and I can't see
      through."
  "It's snow," said the Sun, "just snow."

"But I say, Mr. Sun, are the Robins here?"
  "Maybe," said the Sun, "maybe."
"There wasn't a bird when you called last year."
  "Come out," said the Sun, "and see!"

The Snowdrop sighed, for she liked her nap,
  And there wasn't a bird in sight,
But she popped out of bed in her white night-cap;
  "That's right," said the Sun, "that's right!"

And soon as that small night-cap was seen,
  A Robin began to sing,
The air grew warm, and the grass turned green,
  " 'Tis Spring!" laughed the Sun, " 'tis Spring! '

—Isabel Ecclestone Mackay.

Playing the Poem

It will take four boys and girls to play this poem, because you will need a robin to whistle and a good reader to read the parts that the sun and the snowdrop do not say.

Which of the four boys and girls will say such parts as, "said the Sun"?

---

7. THE SUNFLOWER

Why do most flowers turn toward the sun? This is another of nature's secrets; to explain it, the Greeks, long, long ago, told the beautiful story of Clytie.

Clytie was a sea-maiden, so the old Greek stories tell us. She lived at the bottom of the ocean. The white sea sand was her carpet, a beautiful shell was her bed, and the sea-weed was her pillow.

One morning Clytie arose, put on her moss-green dress, and went to ride in her sea-shell boat. A pair of fishes drew her over the beautiful sea bottom. They swam round rocks with sharp, ragged edges, and they passed through forests

of sea-weed and coral. Indeed, so long and pleasant was the ride that Clytie fell asleep, and she did not awaken until a big wave rolled her boat upon the shore of a green island.

Then the little maiden opened her brown eyes very wide, for she had never before seen the land.

There was green grass at her feet, and such flowers as never grew in her garden at the bottom of the deep sea. In the trees were birds whose songs sounded sweeter than the music of the waves that had so often lulled her to sleep.

Across the blue sky rode the Sun king in a chariot which shone like blazing gold. Clytie saw that all living things looked up and smiled when the golden chariot rolled above the earth.

66 OUT OF DOORS

"Oh, that I were a land child!" she said; "then I too might gaze upon the Sun king the whole day long."

Day after day the sea-maiden came to the island. There she stood hour after hour, watching the bright Sun king until his golden chariot sank into the western sea.

But one evening Clytie found that she could not move. Behold, she was no longer a maid of the sea. Her dress was but a slender green stalk with dark green leaves. Her yellow hair had become a mass of golden petals. From their midst looked down the brown eyes of Clytie, no longer a sea-maiden, but a beautiful Sunflower with its face turned toward the sun.

—Author Unknown.

Making Stories

It is fun to make up stories, as the Greeks did, about nature's secrets.

A boy made up a story to explain how the stars came to be in the sky. He said:

"One day a little girl asked the Sun king to stay all night, because she liked him so much.

"He said he could not stay all night, because he had to visit the children on the other side of the earth.

"But the Sun king liked the little girl, so he told his servants to light candles for her every night."

8. THE PROCESSION

The flower girls, the bridesmaids, the bride herself, the bride's father, and all the people who march at a wedding make a beautiful procession. But more beautiful still is the procession the flowers make as they slip by. Make a picture of this pretty scene, first one flower, then the other.

When the snow has gone away
Maypinks blossom where it lay,

And before the Maypink's gone
Dancing windflowers hurry on:

All the violet-buds are made
Long before the windflowers fade.

Then before the violets go
Yellow dandelions grow:

And before they ever die
Buttercups are growing high,

Then the daisies hurry up,
Each beside a buttercup:

Little pink wild roses follow,
And in every sunny hollow

Black-eyed Susans grow up tall
Long before the roses fall.

Clovers blossom pink and steady
Till the goldenrod is ready:

Purple asters last of all
Wait until the late, late fall,

Till the snow comes flying down
Once again on field and town.

—Margaret Widdemer.

9. FLOWERS THAT TELL TIME

The flowers in "The Procession" can tell us the time of
year, but there are some flowers that tell us the time of
day. Can you guess how dandelions, morning glories,
four-o'clocks, and moon flowers can tell us the time? The
story will tell you whether you have guessed correctly.

Down in the grass plot of a pretty garden
grew a little dandelion. He wore a green jacket,
and his head was covered with sunny, yellow
curls.

In the morning he stood up boldly, lifting
his jolly little face to catch the dewdrops. In

this way he took his morning bath, and he found it very refreshing. At dusk he put on his green night-gown and went to bed very early.

The mothers said, as they called the children from their play, "See, there is the good dandelion! He knows when it is time to go to bed."

As the dandelion grew older, his yellow curls turned white. Then the children would blow—one, two, three times. If all the hairs blew away, it was a sign that Mother wanted them at once.

If there were ten hairs left, the children said, "Mother wants us at ten o'clock."

If but two hairs remained, they said, "Mother will expect us at two o'clock."

When the children awoke in the morning, they saw the morning-glory cups peeping in at the windows. "Six o'clock! Time to get up!" they said. "The morning glories are calling us."

Every afternoon the four-o'clocks bloomed. Their red and white flowers told the children that their father would soon be home.

In the evening the moon flowers unfolded their great white blossoms on the vines that clambered over the porch. "Now it is bed-time," said the children, "for the moon flowers are looking down at us."

All day long the time flowers, like our clocks, are telling us the time of day.

—Kate Louise Brown.

Thinking about the Story

Can you think, now, why the Greeks called the sun a king? Perhaps it is that the sun rules the earth. This story tells us how he rules the flowers. It's the sun that makes the dandelions wake up. He makes the birds fly south in the fall, too. He makes us dress warmly in winter.

Can you find ten other ways in which the sun rules the earth?

10. MOON SONG

Nature makes interesting pictures for us. Near Vancouver there is a mountain that looks like two lions. In Muskoka there is a tree that looks like an old man with an umbrella. What does the moon look like? The writer thinks that the moonbeams on the water look like nets, with which the moon man fishes for beautiful things in the sea.

Zoon, zoon, cuddle and croon—
  Over the crinkling sea,
The moon man flings him a silvered net
  Fashioned of moonbeams three.

And some folk say, when the net lies long
  And the midnight hour is ripe,
The moon man fishes for some old song
  That fell from a sailor's pipe.

And some folk say that he fishes the bars
  Down where the dead ships lie,
Looking for lost little baby stars
  That slid from the slippery sky.

And the waves roll out, and the waves roll in,
  And the nodding night wind blows,
But why the moon man fishes the sea
  Only the moon man knows.

Zoon, zoon, net of the moon
    Rides on the wrinkling sea;
Bright is the fret and shining wet,
    Fashioned of moonbeams three.

And some folk say, when the great net gleams
    And the waves are dusky blue,
The moon man fishes for two little dreams
    He lost when the world was new.

And some folk say, in the late night hours
    While the long fin-shadows slide,
The moon man fishes for cold sea flowers
    Under the tumbling tide.

And the waves roll out, and the waves roll in,
    And the gray gulls dip and doze,
But why the moon man fishes the sea
    Only the moon man knows.

Zoon, zoon, cuddle and croon—
    Over the crinkling sea,
The moon man flings him a silvered net
    Fashioned of moonbeams three.

And some folk say that he follows the flecks
    Down where the last light flows,

Fishing for two round gold-rimmed "specs"
  That blew from his button-like nose.

And some folk say, while the salt sea foams
  And the silver net lines snare,
The moon man fishes for carven combs
  That float from the mermaids' hair.

And the waves roll out, and the waves roll in,
  And the nodding night wind blows,
But why the moon man fishes the sea
  Only the moon man knows.

—MILDRED PLEW MERRYMAN.

READING A LULLABY

The poem is a lullaby; try to read it with long, low swings in your voice, like a cradle rocking.

You will like the sound of the poem if different pupils read each of the verses which begin, "And some folk say—." The whole class should read the other verses together. The class will be a choir again, but this time you will have six soloists. Will you need a choir leader?

11. THE BROOK THAT FOUND THE SEA

Sun and soil could not make things grow without the sea. Clouds are formed over the sea and are blown across the land to water it. Some of the rain water runs away to make a brook that hurries back to the sea, its home.

Once upon a time a little brook set out to find the sea.

At first it had a pleasant time. It ran through wide, green pastures. There cows grazed peacefully, and little lambs frisked gaily under the shade of the trees.

The little brook sang to itself a cheerful tune. Birds darted down to drink from it or to take a morning bath. Pretty little wild flowers, pink and white, and blue and yellow, sprang up on each side.

Children came, too, bringing paper boats. These they sailed upon the little brook, shouting and laughing to see how fast it carried the boats along. But the little brook left all this behind as it hurried on in search of the sea.

At last it came to a huge fallen tree that lay across its path. "I wonder," said the little brook, "if I can push that log out of the way."

It tried with all its might, but the tree would not budge. It held the brook back.

At last the little brook cried out, "If I don't find some way to get past this log, it will turn me into a pond. I don't want to be a pond! Ponds stand still so long that at last they dry up, and they never find the sea."

So the brook ran to one end of the log, but it could not get past. It ran to the other, and wriggled and twisted until it made a tiny crack. It kept on twisting until the little crack grew wider. At last, with a little shout, the brook forced its way through and left the log behind.

"Now," it sang, "all my troubles are over, and I shall soon find the sea."

Just then it came to a high cliff. "What shall I do now?" asked the brook. "If I leap down to those rocks, I may be dashed in spray and never get to the sea."

Suddenly the brave little brook gave a running leap and went over the edge of the cliff.

The rocks did dash the brook into rainbow-coloured spray that filled the air with mist for a while. But the little drops came together

again, saying to one another, "Here I am! Where are you? Let us hurry on our way!"

The way now led through dark and rocky glens. It was very lonely and wild. Once or twice the little brook grew homesick, as it remembered the green pastures, and the cows, and the lambs, and the flowers, and the children who had sailed the boats. But far, far away the billows seemed to be calling, "Come and join us, little brook!" So it hastened on.

It was growing cold, very cold. The little brook tried to keep away the ice. But little frost slivers began to form along the edges, and at last the brook became a prisoner.

"Oh, it is hard to be stopped when I am near enough to hear the sound of the sea!" it cried. "But perhaps this will teach me patience. I have never had patience, I know."

The winter was long and cold. But one day a blue-bird sang. The sun grew warm, and the ice began to melt. It was spring!

The little brook began to bubble and sing. And it started off again toward the sea. It ran down a steep hill and through a long valley. Then, beyond a bar of shining sand, it saw the sea, calm and blue and beautiful. The brook ran faster, singing for joy, and the sea sent out little wavelets to meet it.

—FRANCES WRIGHT.

HAVING FUN AT THE SAND-TABLE

"We know just what to do with this story," said one class.

They decided to tell the story of the brook on the sand-table. When they were finished, they had made a brook and a sea of blue paper; cardboard cows and lambs in the fields; flowers on the banks; children sailing boats; and everything the brook saw on its journey to the sea.

12. "PEACE, BE STILL"

And the same day, when the even was come, He saith unto them, "Let us pass over unto the other side."

And when they had sent away the multitude, they took Him even as He was in the ship. And there were also with Him other little ships.

And there arose a great storm of wind, and the waves beat into the ship, so that it was now full.

And He was in the hinder part of the ship, asleep on a pillow: and they awake Him, and say unto Him, "Master, carest thou not that we perish?"

And He arose, and rebuked the wind, and said unto the sea, "Peace, be still." And the wind ceased, and there was a great calm.

And He said unto them, "Why are ye so fearful? how is it that ye have no faith?"

And they feared exceedingly, and said one to another, "What manner of man is this, that even the wind and the sea obey him?"

—The Bible.

STORIES, OLD & NEW

1. THE LAND OF STORY-BOOKS

A boy, whose name was Robert, liked to play at books that he had read. In the poem he tells you about his play. Can you tell what kind of books he read?

At evening, when the lamp is lit,
Around the fire my parents sit;
They sit at home, and talk and sing,
And do not play at anything.

Now, with my little gun, I crawl
All in the dark along the wall,
And follow round the forest track
Away behind the sofa back.

There in the night, where none can spy,
All in my hunter's camp I lie,

And play at books that I have read,
Till it is time to go to bed.

These are the hills, these are the woods,
These are my starry solitudes;
And there the river, by whose brink
The roaring lions come to drink.

I see the others far away,
As if in firelit camp they lay;
And I, like to an Indian scout,
Around their party prowled about.

So, when my nurse comes in for me,
Home I return across the sea;
And go to bed with backward looks
To my dear land of Story-books.

—ROBERT LOUIS STEVENSON.

ABOUT STORIES

Which of these words tells the kind of stories that
Robert read: funny, fairy, hunting? Find two lines in
the poem that show that your word is the right one.

Think of a word to tell what kind of stories you like
best to read.

Which story have you liked best so far in your Reader?

Write the names of the five best stories you have ever
read.

2. THE LITTLE LADY'S ROSES

To make a friend, one must be a friend. To be a friend, one must do kind, friendly deeds. The story tells how a lady, with her roses, made friends of the children in the village.

Down in the valley was a village where John and Mary lived with their mother and father in a little cottage. There they went to school when the bell rang in the little school-house on week days, and to church when the bells rang in the little church on Sundays.

And up on the hill was a great mansion, where a little lady lived all by herself with her servants. She paced up and down the long flight of stone steps between the cypresses and orange trees, or walked in her rose garden, which was the loveliest in the world.

The hill was high, and the valley was deep, so that people seldom went up or came down. Only a silvery river flowed between the high mansion and the low cottages, and seemed to bind them together.

When they were out of school, Mary helped her mother in the kitchen, and before she was ten she could bake little pies fit for a queen. And John dug in the garden with his father, and before he was twelve could raise cabbages fit for a king. In their free time the children played in the fields with their school-fellows, or paddled in the shallow pools of the river as it flowed down the middle of the valley. And they were very happy.

One hot June day, as they were splashing in the shallows, they saw in the distance two tiny specks floating toward them.

"Here come the boats!" cried John.

"With red and white sails," said Mary.

"I'll have the red one," said John; and Mary said, "I'll have the white."

But as the tiny craft came nearer, the children saw that they were not boats, but roses. They had never seen such roses for colour, size, and perfume. John captured the red rose and Mary the white one, and home they ran with their prizes.

When their parents saw the roses, the father said, "By my Shovel and Hoe! If I could grow roses like that in my garden, I'd be a proud man!"

And the mother cried, "Dear bless my Cherry Tart! If I could have roses like those in the home, I'd be a glad woman!"

Then the father asked, "Where did you get them, children?"

"They came down the river from the top of the hill," said John.

"Ah!" sighed the father, "then they came from the little lady's rose garden, and are not for people like us."

And he went out to hoe cabbages, while the mother rolled her paste.

But John and Mary stole out of the cottage, and John said to Mary, "Let us find the little lady's rose garden, and beg her for a rose tree to make our parents proud and happy."

"How shall we find it?" said Mary.

"We'll take the road up the hill that the roses took down."

"What road is that?" said Mary.

"The river," said John.

So they followed the river uphill until they came near the top, and were stopped by a big iron gate that led to the longest flight of steps they had ever seen. On the steps the little lady herself paced slowly up, and when she reached the fountain at the top, she turned and paced slowly down again. At the bottom of the steps she saw the faces of John and Mary pressed against the bars.

"What are you doing?" said John.

"Counting the steps," said the little lady.

"Why?" said Mary.

"Because I have nothing else to do," said the little lady.

"Why don't you go and hoe cabbages?" said John.

"My head gardener won't let me."

"Why don't you go and bake pies?" said Mary.

"My head cook would be cross with me."

"Father lets me hoe cabbages!" said John.

"Mother lets me bake pies!" said Mary.

"How lucky you are!" said the little lady. "Who are you?"

"John," said John.

"Mary," said Mary.

"Where do you come from?"

"The village in the valley."

"What have you come for?"

"A red rose tree for Father," said John.

"A white one for Mother," said Mary.

"Oh!" cried the little lady, "did you find the roses I sent down the river?   How glad I am!"

"Why did you send them down?" asked John.

"To bring someone back. You can't think how dull it is with nobody to play with. If you will stay and play with me, you shall have a rose tree apiece, and my head gardener won't know the difference."

So John and Mary stayed all day with the little lady, playing in her rose garden until they were tired. And she sent them home with a rose tree each, which they took to their parents, saying that they had spent the happiest day of their lives.

But next morning the little lady found counting the steps duller than ever, so, when she reached the gate, she opened it for the very first time and ran down the hill. On reaching the village she went straight to John and Mary's cottage, walked in, and said:

"I want to bake pies and hoe cabbages."

"Bless my Apple Dumpling, so you shall!" said the mother.

So first the little lady got her hands as white as flour, and then as black as earth. And, when she went home, she took a cabbage and a pasty with her, and said it was the happiest day of her life.

After this, whenever she was lonely, she knew she had only to run down the hill herself, or set a rose sailing to bring up a child. A white rose brought a girl, and a red rose brought a boy.

And sometimes she gathered a whole skirtful of roses and set them afloat; and on those days every child in the village was to be seen running up the hill to the little lady's rose garden.   —Eleanor Farjeon.

A Paper Garden

1. Make the little lady's garden out of paper. Use heavy paper for the hillside, and on it paste green paper cut like fringes to show the grass. Beautiful roses may be made from crêpe paper. The steps, the fountain, and the wall with its gate may be made with cardboard coloured with crayon. The little lady and the children may be placed in the garden, too. Can you make dolls out of wire and clay, or paper? The dolls should have costumes.

2. Copy these sentences into your exercise books. But first, find the right parts to match.

People seldom went up or came down, because	she took home a cabbage and a pasty.
John and Mary thought	they had a rose tree.
They thought their parents would be happy if	the hill was high, and the valley was deep.
The lonely little lady counted the steps because	the roses were little boats.
It was the happiest day of her life, when	she had nothing else to do.

3. THE ELVES AND THE SHOEMAKER

We look into the workshop of a Shoemaker. A little old man sits in the middle of the room with a shoemaker's last before him, in his hand a shoe which he is stitching. The Shoemaker's face is lighted by a single candle which stands on the corner of a table beside him. By the light of the candle we notice in one corner of the room a cupboard with dishes in it, in another corner a stove. In front of the Shoemaker lies a piece of leather on the floor, and beside the leather a box of tools. We guess that the Shoemaker is very poor and that his workshop is also his kitchen. Poor though he is, he is not unhappy, for as he works he hums to himself. All that we can hear is the tune, but if we listen carefully, we may imagine we hear the words:

> *Stitch—Stitch—*
> *The world walks long,*
> *And the world walks soon,*
> *And all folk march*
> *To the cobbler's tune.*
> *Stitch—Stitch—*
> *To the cobbler's tune.*

We like the old man because he is so happy at his work, but we are sorry for him because he is so poor and must work so late.

The door at the back of the room opens, and in the half light a little old lady appears. She comes into the room and busies herself. She speaks.

LITTLE OLD LADY.   The night is late, Husband; you must leave your work until to-morrow.

SHOEMAKER.   But the shoes are not yet finished, my dear, and if a gentleman should come for shoes to-morrow, I should have none to sell. Then he would say I must be a lazy workman and he would not come back.

LITTLE OLD LADY.   Lazy! Good stars, Husband! Have you not been working since first the robin sang in the apple tree this morning? Now you must come to bed. (*She moves over to the table and straightens the cloth.*) I have heard the fairy pipes in the meadow ring, and you know the fairies may not come to dance again if they should cross our candle beam shining through the window on the grass.

SHOEMAKER.   That is so.   We must not frighten the fairies. (*As he talks, he tidies up his working things.*) I should not mind to scare away the elves; they are almost as bad as the pixies. Did you hear their mischief last night? They kept me awake till morning, almost, tinkling with their hammers on the window glass.

LITTLE OLD LADY. Indeed I did hear them. And then after you went to the window and opened it to frighten them away, you had no more than dozed off to sleep than the young mischiefs climbed through the window, jumped on the bed, and pulled your night-cap over your eyes. But I went "Pooh"—like that—with my breath. You would have laughed to see them so startled. (*The Little Old Lady, remembering, laughs to herself. We like her laugh because it is like a blackbird's song.*)

SHOEMAKER (*laughing, too*). I'll make a magic and turn them into pixies if they don't behave. (*He takes up the candle and follows the Little Old Lady to the door. There he stops, and turns around as if to take a final loving look at the unfinished shoes.*) Pixies! (*He goes off chuckling. Evidently he likes the idea.*)

(*There is a quiet for a moment. The moonlight shines through the window, and we can see everything in the room even more easily than when the candle was there. The moonlight grows*

*brighter, as if someone had hung the moon just
outside the window. We wait for the quiet to end.)*

TINY ELF. (*His head bobs up over the window-sill.*) Did you hear what he said?

TEENY ELF. (*He bobs up, too.*) Pixies!

TEENY-WEENY ELF. Pixies indeed!

(*Quiet a moment; heads very still.*)

TINY. One! (*Up they come with their palms
on the window-sill.*)

TEENY. Two! (*Right feet beside their palms.*)

TEENY-WEENY. Three! (*With a bound they
are in the room.*)

(*Pause. They look this way. They look that
way. They look at one another. But Teen-Weeny,
being in the middle, has to look two ways at
once, and he just about twists his head off.
They are very ragged elves, with many tatters
and few patches. Probably they have not had
new suits of clothes for a thousand years.*)

TINY. Let's put salt in his sugar.

TEENY. He hasn't any salt.

TEENY-WEENY. He hasn't any sugar.

ALL TOGETHER. Poo-oo-oo-oor, poor man.

TEENY. Cinnabeck in his tillicum would be
pretty bad.

TINY. Silly.

TEENY-WEENY. Don't be absurd. (*He tries to make his voice grown up, but it squeaks instead.*)

(*The elves think. They think for a long time. They think very hard. Their faces become all screwed up with thinking.*)

TEENY-WEENY. I have an idea!

TINY. No!

TEENY-WEENY. Yes.

TEENY. Excellent!

(*They put their heads together and their arms about one another's shoulders. They talk in very loud whispers, but we cannot hear what they say. All that we can make out is "Ps-s-s-s-s Ps Ps Ps-s-s-s-s-s." After a moment they part.*)

TINY AND TEENY-WEENY (*shaking hands*). Agreed.

TEENY AND TEENY-WEENY (*shaking hands*). Agreed.

TINY AND TEENY (*also s.h.*). Agreed.

ALL TOGETHER. Hurrah! (*A very solemn cheer.*)

(*Then what a hurry and scurry! Great sheets of leather fly through the air. Hammers and lasts and awls come tumbling down to the floor with an awful clatter. Chairs are upset in the bustle. The frying pan falls off the stove, and the table falls over on its back and kicks its legs in the*

*air.   In a moment things quiet down, and we
see the elves sitting cross-legged on the floor—
Tiny at the right, Teeny at the left, and Teeny-
Weeny in the middle.   They are pounding with
their little hammers, rat-a-tat-tat, rat-a-tat-tat, and
as they work they sing:*

> *Hi-diddle-diddle
> The toe's in the middle,
> The heel's in the front of the shoe.
> Sew the sole on the hole,
> Tick a tack on the sole,
> Add the buckle and then—that'll DO.*

*Elves, of course, work very quickly, and at
the end of every line three shoes fly through the
air and come down to the floor with a bang—
three bangs.   At the end of each verse three new
pairs of shoes litter the floor.*

*In the middle of it all the door at the back
opens.   We put our fingers to our mouths for fear
the elves will be frightened away, but they are so
busy, and they make so much noise, that they
neither see nor hear.   At one side of the door
appears a red night-cap, followed by the Shoemaker's sleepy face.   When he sees what he sees,
his mouth opens.   His eyes open.   His night-*

cap nearly falls off. He turns his head and wiggles his finger, beckoning the Little Old Lady.

On the other side of the door appears another night-cap and the Little Old Lady's face under it. They look at the elves. They look at each other. We can see that they are all bottled up and want to explode because they are so excited. They turn and hug each other. Then they whisper and make a great many signs with their hands. The Little Old Lady says something. The Shoemaker bobs his head. They disappear.)

TINY. We haven't had so much fun since the time we played with Goldilocks and the bears.

TEENY. The trouble with us elves is that we never have half enough to do. That's why we get into mischief.

TEENY-WEENY. Well, we've plenty to do now. Stop talking and get to work. I'm a shoe-and-a-half ahead of you.

(So the shoes fly fast and faster. Then the shoemaker and his wife re-appear in the doorway. They have something over their arms, and they tiptoe as quietly as they possibly can into the middle of the room, and hang things on the table legs. We see what they are now: little blue trousers, red jackets, and funny little pointed

*caps.   The table legs amuse us with the caps
perched on them, but we can only smile because
the elves would hear us if we were to laugh.
The Shoemaker and his wife tiptoe out again,
and hide behind the door-sills with only their
heads peeking out, he on this side, she on that.)*

*(After a moment Tiny pauses to stretch.   The
colour of the clothing catches his eye.)*

TINY.   Brothers!   *(They stop work.)*   Look!

TEENY.   Well, I'll be swithered.

TEENY-WEENY.   Bless my shoe-buckles.

(They look down at their ragged clothes.)

TEENY.   We haven't had new suits since the
time we coasted down the pyramids.

TINY.   Nobody ever thinks of elves wearing
pants and jackets.

TEENY-WEENY.   If you stopped talking, we
could try them on.

*(Up they get.   But it has been so long since
they have tried clothes on that they hardly know
where to begin.   Tiny gets his leg through a
neck.   Teeny tries to pull on the trousers over
his head and gets stuck, of course.   But they
laugh and dance and help each other out and
have a merry time.   When they are dressed, they
straighten the table, join hands, and dance around*

it, singing their song. Then they straighten a chair and dance around it. They straighten the other chair and dance around it.)

TEENY-WEENY. One. Two. Straighten the shoes.

TINY. Three. Four. Tidy the floor.

TEENY. Five. Six. A couple of licks. (*He picks up a stick and pretends to drive his brothers to work. In no time the floor is cleared, and dozens of shoes stand in neat pairs around the wall.*)

(*The Shoemaker sneezes. The elves vanish.*)

SHOEMAKER (*coming into the room*). Can you believe it?

LITTLE OLD LADY (*following him*). The poor wee things.

SHOEMAKER. We can be selling shoes for the rest of our lives.

LITTLE OLD LADY. And you, Husband, will not need to work from dawn to night.

SHOEMAKER. It is nearly daylight now. Do you hear the robin? Listen.

(*Tiny's head appears above the window-sill. He sneezes. Up pops Teeny, and sneezes. Then Teeny-Weeny, and sneezes. The three elves sneeze together. The curtain is drawn quickly to keep out the draught.*)

—*Dramatized from* JACOB AND WILHELM GRIMM.

4. THE CAPTAIN AND THE PROPHET

A certain disease, called leprosy, is very hard to cure, and in the olden days, only by a miracle could a person be rid of it. Here is the miracle story of how one man was cured.

Now Naaman, captain of the host of the king of Syria, was a great man with his master, and honourable; he was also a mighty man in valour; but he was a leper.

And the Syrians had gone out, and had brought away captive out of the land of Israel a little maid; and she waited on Naaman's wife.

And she said unto her mistress, "Would God my lord were with the prophet that is in Samaria! for he would recover him of his leprosy."

And one went in, and told his lord, saying, Thus and thus said the maid that is of the land of Israel.

And the king of Syria said, "Go to, go, and I will send a letter unto the king of Israel." And he departed.

So Naaman came with his horses and with his chariot, and stood at the door of the house of Elisha.

And Elisha sent a messenger unto him, saying, "Go and wash in Jordan seven times, and thy flesh shall come again to thee, and thou shalt be clean."

But Naaman was wroth, and went away, and said, "Behold, I thought, He will surely come out to me, and stand, and call on the name of the Lord his God, and strike his hand over the place, and recover the leper.

"Are not Abana and Pharpar, rivers of Damascus, better than all the waters of Israel? may I not wash in them, and be clean?" So he turned, and went away in a rage.

And his servants came near, and spake unto him, and said, "My father, if the prophet had bid thee do some great thing, wouldst thou not have done it? how much rather then, when he saith to thee, 'Wash, and be clean?'"

Then went he down, and dipped himself seven times in Jordan, according to the saying of the man of God; and his flesh came again like unto the flesh of a little child, and he was clean.

—THE BIBLE.

BIBLE STORIES

The whole story of Naaman is not given in your Reader. Choose a boy or a girl who is a very good reader to read to the class the rest of the story from the Bible.

Ask your teacher to read to you the story of how Elisha became a prophet.

5. HOW FIRE CAME TO THE INDIANS

How did fire begin? Did you ever wonder? The Indians used to wonder, too; and to answer the question, their story-tellers made up the following tale about the way fire came to them.

Thousands of years ago the Skookum sisters had the only fire in the world. There were Skookum One, Skookum Two, and Skookum Three, ugly, mean old crones who lived on the mountain-top. They were so mean that, even when the Indians in the valley were freezing to death, they would not share their fire with them.

Now in those days the animals were the friends of man and did everything they could to protect him. Coyote, especially, liked the Indians so well that he sometimes had the idea he would go and live with them. But whether he lived with them or not, he decided that something would have to be done immediately about this business of fire. So he called the other animals together and made his plans.

Part way down the mountain-side was an old pine tree.

"Lynx," said Coyote, "you climb up there; and don't snarl."

Half way down the mountain-side was an old elm tree.

"Squirrel," said Coyote, "you scamper up there; and don't chatter."

Nearly at the bottom of the mountain was a swamp.

"Frog," said Coyote, "you hop in there; and don't croak."

At the foot of the mountain was a Wood, where the Indians lived. Coyote went up close to Wood and whispered in his ear. Wood nodded his head. Coyote smiled, rubbed his paws with satisfaction, and turned to creep cautiously up the mountain-side.

On the mountain-top he found the Skookums huddled over the ember, warming the ends of their noses, which were already as red as coals. Coyote lay down behind a stump to wait. Skookums have to eat, of course, and they have to sleep, but while One slept, Two ate, and Three guarded the fire. When Three slept, One ate, and Two guarded the fire. Never did they leave the fire without a guard.

Then came Skookum One to guard the fire, while Three gnawed her bone. Coyote was growing impatient. He had neither slept nor eaten

FROG THREW THE FIRE TO WOOD

for two nights and two days, and the sight of that bone was almost more than he could bear. Finally he could stand it no longer. He crept as close to the Skookums as he could.

"Skookum-jookum!" he cried.

The startled Skookums jumped so high that, before they had hit the ground again, Coyote had grabbed the fire.

Away he ran, with a Skookum after him. Down the mountain-side he tumbled. He had almost reached the pine tree when the Skookum caught him by the tip of the tail. It turned white immediately, and so it is even to this day.

But Lynx jumped from the tree, snatched the fire, and bounded down the mountain-side, with the Skookum after him.

He had just reached the elm tree by the big rock when the Skookum caught up to him. Lynx was so angry that his eyes glowed like coals. That is why they shine at night even to this day.

Quickly Lynx tossed the fire to Squirrel, and Squirrel jumped from branch to branch down the mountain-side. The fire was so hot that it curled his tail up over his back, and there it is even to this day.

The Skookum could not catch Squirrel in the tree-tops, and he reached Frog. Frog caught the fire in his mouth, and away he hopped down the mountain-side. But the Skookum caught Frog by the tail. Froggie croaked, gave a tremendous hop, and escaped, but he left his tail with the Skookum. That is why frogs have no tails even to this day.

To save the fire, Frog threw it to Wood, and Wood swallowed it. Then the Skookums were as cross as sticks because they did not know how to get the fire out of Wood. But Coyote knew, and when the Skookums had gone raging back to their cave on the mountain-top, he showed the Indians how to rub two pieces of wood together to turn the wood into fire. And that is the way Indians make fire, even to this day.

—*Retold from* KATHARINE B. JUDSON.

FINDING THINGS OUT

The Indians thought that wood burns because it swallowed fire. Ask your teacher to tell you the real reason.

Do you remember how rain is made? Turn to page 55, if you have forgotten.

Write down five other questions to which you would like to know the answers. How can you find the answers?

Why is this story something like the story on page 64?

6. ANDROCLES AND THE LION

A kind deed is worth doing just for its own sake, but sometimes it brings a rich reward, as in this famous story.

In the great city of Rome, there lived many years ago a poor slave named Androcles. Very terrible things he suffered at the hands of his cruel master, until, unable to bear his miseries any longer, he ran away and hid in the forests that lay beyond the city walls. But little could he find to eat in the woods, and each day growing weaker, he at last crept into a cave to die. Stretched upon the floor, he fell into a deep sleep, whence he was awakened by the roaring of a lion that entered the cave, limping, and in great pain.

Androcles saw that there was a large thorn in the lion's paw. Though much afraid, he took the paw in his hands and, with a quick, strong pull, drew out the thorn. At once the pain was eased. The lion licked Androcles's hands, rubbed his head against him, and lay down at his feet. Androcles was no longer afraid. That night, lion and slave slept side by side.

Next morning the lion went out into the woods, but soon came back bringing with him

food for Androcles.   This he did for many days, and the slave was happier in the cave than he had ever been in his master's house.

At length, some Roman soldiers, travelling through the woods, came upon Androcles and brought him back to Rome.   According to the law, slaves who ran away must fight with wild animals in a ring before the people.   To make these animals fiercer no food was given to them for days beforehand.

Into the ring, then, they brought Androcles on an appointed day.   Thousands of people sat above on raised seats to watch the fight. No one spoke a word of pity for the poor slave. A door in the wall opened, and a hungry lion leaped in. With a roar, he rushed toward the slave, who leaped lightly aside as the animal sprang at him. Then a strange thing happened. There was a cry of joy from the slave. He threw his arms about the lion, and the lion licked his face. Leaning against him, Androcles faced the people. The old friends had met once more.

The crowd gazed in astonishment, and asked Androcles what magic power he had over the beast. Then Androcles told them of his misery with his master, and of his happy days in the cave. "I am a man," said he, "yet no man has been kind to me. It has remained for a wild beast to love and protect me." The hearts of the people were moved, and they cried with a loud voice: "Life for the slave and the lion! Freedom for both."

So Androcles became a free man, and for years afterwards he and his lion were among the sights of old Rome.

—A ROMAN TALE.

THINKING ABOUT THE STORY

Read the story again, and make five sentences that tell the whole story. The first sentence might be, "A slave named Androcles ran away."

Write the five sentences. Ask another boy or girl in the class whether your sentences tell the story.

7. THE MAN WHO DID NOT LIKE MUSIC

In one of the books in your class-room library, you will find a map of Canada. On the map find the place where you live. Away to the north find the cold land where the Eskimos live. From that land came the story of "The Man Who Did Not Like Music."

There was once an Eskimo named Tig-gak, who did not like music. When his brothers sang songs, or beat upon their tom-toms, he went out and walked by himself.

One day, however, when seal-hunting in his kayak, he heard some music which he liked. Tig-gak looked up, and he looked down, he looked here, and he looked there, but he could not find where the sound came from.

Farther out on the sea, he saw some men sailing in a u-miak. They were going against the wind, yet no one was rowing. Indeed, the boatmen were resting on their oars, and singing a song. It was the song Tig-gak had liked.

At the end of each verse was a chorus:

"Kanga-tarsa! Kanga-tarsa!
Imakaja! Ah, ha, ha!"

These words meant:

"Aloft! Aloft!
Let us be taken aloft!"

When they sang this chorus, the boat rose a little above the water and went skimming along the surface of the waves. When the new verse began, it sank back into the waves; and thus it went on, time about. So great was the speed of the u-miak that Tig-gak could scarcely keep up with it. But he rowed very hard and managed to bring his kayak alongside.

"Good sirs," he cried, "I like your singing. If it please you, let me travel with you."

The steersman replied that he might come with them, if he could keep their pace. To aid him, he flung out a line to Tig-gak, and Tig-gak tied his kayak to the end of the line and was towed along.

Soon the rowers began singing again:

"Aloft! Aloft!
Let us be taken aloft!"

This time the u-miak and the kayak rose clean up out of the water, and came flying

landward till they rested on a high mountain.
They stayed on this mountain for a while;
then once more they rose into the air, and
this time they went on till they came to a
camping-ground on a wide plain. Here they
sank down and down till their skin boats
rested on the snow; whereupon the Singing
People got out, and so likewise did Tig-gak.

They found a hut made ready for them.
It was built of stone and sods, and had
twelve posts. Inside were a cooking-stove and
plenty of lamps, and a ledge with many beds.

The Singing People made Tig-gak welcome in
their hut, and he lived with them for a long
time.

By and by, however, he began to think of
home. "My brothers will be missing me," he
said to himself, and he asked his kind friends
if he might go back. The Singing People
said he must do as he wished. They filled
his kayak with food and taught him their
magic song:

"Kanga-tarsa! Kanga-tarsa!
Imakaja! Ah, ha, ha!"

Tig-gak said these words over and over
again, till he knew them by heart. Then he
put on his fur coat and hood, his gloves, and
his kayak jacket, and having said good-bye
to the Singing People, he got into his kayak.
"Kanga-tarsa!   Kanga-tarsa!"   they   all
sang, "Imakaja! Ah, ha, ha!" and Tig-gak
rose up through the air, and turned his face
homeward.

All went well with him until he reached
the high mountain. There, feeling weary, he
thought he would have a nap. Still seated in

his kayak, he fell fast asleep, and when he awoke, he had forgotten the words of the song!

Try as he might he could not recall them. "Imakaga!" he cried—"No, not quite right! Kamajaja!—No, not quite right!"

Each time he sang, the kayak gave a jerk which brought it nearer to the edge of the mountain, and at length it leaped right over the top, and began falling, falling!

"I am lost!" thought Tig-gak, "I shall never see my home again!" But as he was about to crash, the words of the song came back to him. "Kanga-tarsa!" he sang joyfully, "Imakaja! Ah, ha, ha!" At once the kayak righted itself and, rising high in the air, sailed swiftly onward to the coast.

Far down, on the shore, he saw his brothers' hut, and full of joy he pointed the nose of the kayak toward it. Then, diving downward, he crashed right through the roof, and into their midst!

Just then his brothers were seated on the bench for supper. They were eating their fish and throwing the scraps to their dogs. "Ho! Ho! what is this?" they cried, starting up, and all the dogs began barking. But soon they saw that it was Tig-gak.

His brothers were glad to see him again, and he was glad to see them. He sat on the bench and told them of his adventures. When he had finished, his brothers looked at one another. One of them said, "When we sing our songs, O Tig-gak, we, too, are lifted from the earth; we are borne away to distant places; and we are glad, as you were, when the music saved you from the rocks at the foot of the high mountain."

Then the brothers sang, and with them Tig-gak sang,

> "Kanga-tarsa! Kanga-tarsa!
> Imakaja! Ah, ha, ha!"

But this time the song did not take them aloft, except that their hearts were lifted up in gladness.

—An Eskimo Folk-Tale.

Making Music

Hum to yourself a tune that suits the chorus that Tig-gak liked so much. Hum your tune to the class so that the class may select the one that suits the words best. Then the whole class may sing the two lines of the chorus.

Do you think Tig-gak would like your tune?

8. A BABY'S ADVENTURE

Adventures are always exciting. Here is the story of an adventure that came to a little baby called Jean Lajimodière (zhän la-zhē-mō-dyĕr′). Little Jean found it fun, but his sister and his mother were very frightened. Our country has many stories of adventures with Indians.

In the early days of the West, a French-Canadian family named Lajimodière settled on the plains. Madame Lajimodière was the first white woman to live on the prairie.

One morning Madame Lajimodière hung a pail on her arm, and, as she did so, she spoke to her little daughter.

"I'm going to the river to fill the water barrel, René," she said, "and you must look after your baby brother."

113

Little René was not much more than three years old, but she understood her mother's words quite well, and lisped, "René will sing to baby."

So René sang to the baby, and as she sang, she rocked his cradle very gently. "Sleep little brother, sleep," she sang, and at last the baby closed his blue eyes.

"Now, I'll run down to the river to meet Mama," René said to herself. But before she reached the door, it was opened by an Indian woman.

The woman did not look at René. She went at once to the cradle where the baby was sleeping. Before the little girl knew what was happening, the Indian woman had snatched him up from his cosy bed and wrapped him in her blanket. Then she went quickly out.

The Indian woman was taking her baby brother away! René ran out of the cabin, and as she ran, she cried, "Mama! Mama! A squaw came. She took baby away!"

When Madame Lajimodière heard the child calling, she dropped her pail of water, and hurried up the path that led from the river to the house.

"Quick, Mama, quick!" René called, and pointed down the trail.

"A squaw took baby," she shouted.

In a second Madame Lajimodière was hurrying down the trail after the Indian woman.

"Give me my baby!" she cried as she ran; but the oftener she called, the faster the Indian woman ran.

After they had run for nearly a mile, the Indian woman became tired and began to walk. Madame Lajimodière was tired too, but when she saw that the Indian woman was walking, she ran even faster. At last she overtook her and caught her blanket.

"Give me my baby!" she panted.

The Indian woman turned and looked at Madame Lajimodière, and as she did so, she held the baby tighter in her arms.

"My baby! You've stolen my little Jean," Madame Lajimodière cried.

The Indian woman shook Madame Lajimodière's hand from her blanket. She turned to run again, but she saw that there were tears in the mother's eyes and tears streaming down her cheeks.

The Indian woman's face became very sad, but she held out the baby to his mother. He was smiling and gurgling happily as the white woman began to run back to the cabin. For a few minutes the squaw stood watching her. At last she turned and went slowly down the trail.

Madame Lajimodière did not know the Indian woman's language, and the Indian woman did not know Madame's. It was not until her husband returned from taking his furs to Fort Garry that she learned why the Indian woman had wanted her baby. She had wanted him because she thought he was a baby angel. His eyes were so blue, and his hair was so golden, that the squaw was certain that, if she could carry him to her tribe, her people would always have good luck in their hunting and fishing.

—JESSIE EVELYN MCEWEN.

STUDYING A PICTURE

In the picture on page 113, find five things that show that the story is about "the early days."

Find three ways in which the artist has shown that the woman is an Indian.

In the story find one sentence that describes the picture.

9. THE STORY OF MOSES

In the land of Egypt, very long ago, there
lived a cruel king, who hated the people of
Israel. He gave orders that every one of their
baby boys should be thrown into the river
and drowned.

But there was one little boy whose mother hid him from the king until he was three months old. When she found that she could no longer keep him hidden, she made a basket of bulrushes, like a boat or ark, and rubbed tar and pitch over it to keep the water out. Then early one morning she put her baby into the basket, and laid it among the tall reeds that grew on the bank of the river.

To watch the boy, the child's sister, Miriam, hid behind the reeds, where she could see what happened to him.

Soon the king's daughter came down to the water and walked along the riverside. She saw the little basket floating among the tall reeds, and sent one of her maidens to get it and bring it to her.

When the basket was brought to the princess, the baby was crying, and she was sorry for the poor little boy.

Then Miriam came to the king's daughter and said, "Shall I go and fetch a nurse for the baby, so that she may take care of him for you?" And the king's daughter said, "Yes, go."

So Miriam went, and brought her mother.

When her mother came, the princess said, "Take care of this child for me, and I will pay you." Then the baby's own mother took care of him for the princess.

The king's daughter adopted him as her son, and called him Moses, because this name means, "I drew him out of the water."

When Moses grew up, he was often sad and troubled because he saw that his people had a hard time in Egypt and that the king was very cruel to them. Moses went to the cruel king and asked him to let the people of Israel depart from Egypt; but the king would not let them go. He wanted the people of Israel to stay and work for him. Again and again Moses begged the king to let them go, but still the king refused.

Then Moses prayed to God to punish the king; and God heard the prayer of Moses, and sent swarms of flies and frogs and other pests to cover the land. The cattle perished, and the crops were destroyed. Many of the people fell ill and died.

The king knew that God was angry because the people of Israel had been treated so badly, and at last he said that they might go. So

Moses and his people took their flocks and herds and departed out of Egypt.

As soon as they had started, the king was sorry he had let them go, and he sent an army to bring them back. But God watched over the people of Israel, and they escaped, and the army of Egypt was drowned in the sea.

It was many years before the people of Israel reached the land which became their home. They had to travel through great deserts and over high mountains. They had to fight many enemies. Often they lost their way. Often they were tired and hungry. They murmured against Moses, who was their leader, and were ungrateful.

But Moses was a wise and good leader. When his people complained, he tried to make them see how grateful they should be because they had escaped from Egypt. He gave them good laws and taught them to love God and lead good lives; and at last he brought them to the beautiful land which became their home. Sad to say, he himself never entered that land of promise.

—A Bible Story.

10. THE TAR-BABY

An old Negro, whom the boys and girls called "Uncle Remus," used to tell the children stories about the animals in the woods. Some of the stories the children liked best were tales about Brother Fox and Brother Rabbit. In speaking about Brother Fox and Brother Rabbit, Uncle Remus used to leave out some of the letters, and "Brother" became "Br——er": Brer Fox and Brer Rabbit. Brer Fox was very clever, and tried many tricks to catch Brer Rabbit, but Brer Rabbit was always just a little bit too clever for Brer Fox. The Tar-Baby story tells of one of Brer Rabbit's terrible adventures.

Brer Fox was very angry to think that Brer Rabbit had tricked him so often. And he made up his mind to harm Brer Rabbit somehow or other.

So one day Brer Fox got some tar, and mixed it with turpentine; then he worked it about until he had made it into the shape of a big doll or Tar-Baby. After that he put a tall hat on Tar-Baby's head, and laughed.

"This Tar-Baby will catch Brer Rabbit, I'm thinking!" he chuckled.

He took the Tar-Baby and set it down in the road, and then went to hide in the bushes to see what would happen.

He had not waited long before Brer Rabbit

came along the road — lippitty-clippitty, clip-pitty-lippity—just as cheeky as you please.

Brer Fox lay low. Brer Rabbit came pran-cing along until he saw the Tar-Baby, and then he stood quite still in surprise. The Tar-Baby sat there, as quiet as a mouse, and Brer Fox still lay low.

"Good-morning!" said Brer Rabbit to the Tar-Baby. "Nice weather we're having!"

The Tar-Baby said nothing at all.

"What's the matter with you? Are you deaf?" asked Brer Rabbit. "Because, if you are, I can shout louder!"

The Tar-Baby stayed still, and Brer Fox lay low. "You're stuck-up and proud, that's what you are!" said Brer Rabbit loudly. "I'm going to box your ears, that's what I'm going to do!"

Brer Fox chuckled to himself, but the Tar-Baby said nothing at all.

"I'm going to teach you how to answer when you're spoken to," said Brer Rabbit fiercely. "If you don't take off your hat and say, 'How do you do,' I'm going to hit you hard!"

The Tar-Baby said not a word, and Brer Fox lay low.

Well, Brer Rabbit kept on asking the Tar-Baby questions, and still he got no answer. So at last Brer Rabbit raised his hand, and "blip!" he struck the Tar-Baby on the side of the head. His hand at once stuck in the tar, and he could not pull it out. The tar held it tight. But the Tar-Baby stayed as quiet as ever, and Brer Fox still lay low.

"If you don't let me go, I'll hit you again!" said Brer Rabbit. With that he hit the Tar-Baby with his other hand, and that stuck too! Still the Tar-Baby said nothing at all.

"Let me go before I kick you to pieces!" shouted Brer Rabbit angrily; but the Tar-Baby did not answer a word. It just held on, and when Brer Rabbit kicked with both his feet, it held on to those too! Then Brer Rabbit yelled out that if the Tar-Baby didn't let go, he would butt her in with his head.

And then he butted, and his head got stuck. And now Brer Rabbit couldn't move an inch!

Out came Brer Fox from the bushes.

"How do you do, Brer Rabbit?" cried Brer Fox. "You look rather stuck-up this morning!" And he rolled on the ground, and laughed and laughed till he couldn't laugh any more.

"I expect you'll come and have dinner with me *this* time, Brer Rabbit," said Brer Fox. "I shan't take any excuse!" And then he rolled on the ground and laughed again.

At last he got up, wiped his eyes, and said, "Well, I expect I've got you this time, Brer Rabbit. Perhaps I haven't, but I *think* I have! You've been running round tricking me for a mighty long time. Well, there you are, and there you'll stay till I make a pile of wood and light it up, because I'm going to *roast* you to-day, sure as anything!"

Then Brer Rabbit began to speak in a very low, humble voice.

"I don't care *what* you do with me, Brer Fox," he said, "so long as you don't throw me into that brier-patch. Roast me if you like, but oh, please, don't throw me into that brier-patch!"

"It's too much trouble to make a fire," said Brer Fox, "so I think I'd better *hang* you."

"Hang me as high as you please, Brer Fox," said Brer Rabbit, "but for pity's sake, *don't* throw me into that brier-patch!"

"I haven't got any string," said Brer Fox, "so I expect I'd better *drown* you."

"Drown me as deep as you please, Brer Fox," said Brer Rabbit, "but don't throw me into that brier-patch!"

"There isn't any water near," said Brer Fox, "so I think I'll *skin* you."

"Skin me, do Brer Fox!" said Brer Rabbit. "Tear out my eyes and cut off my legs, but please, *please*, Brer Fox, *don't* throw me into that brier-patch!"

Well, Brer Fox wanted to hurt Brer Rabbit as much as he could, so he thought he *would* throw him into that prickly brier-patch. And he caught him by his hind legs and slung him right into the middle of it!

Brer Rabbit went head over heels, rolling in the brier-patch, and Brer Fox ran up to see what had happened. But when he got there, he saw no Brer Rabbit at all!

But by and by Brer Fox heard somebody calling him, and away up the hill he saw Brer Rabbit. He was sitting cross-legged on a log, combing the tar out of his hair. Then Brer Fox knew he had been tricked again. And he was terribly angry when he heard Brer Rabbit call out,

"I was bred and born in a brier-patch, Brer Fox! Bred and born in a brier-patch!" And off he skipped, as cheeky and merry as ever!

Retold by ENID BLYTON *from "Uncle Remus" by* JOEL CHANDLER HARRIS.

WRITE A PLAY

Make a play out of "The Tar-Baby," and act it. Write the play, first, as "The Sleeping Beauty" is written. You might begin in this way:

"BRER FOX (*chuckling*). This Tar-Baby will catch Brer Rabbit, I'm thinking. (*He sets the Tar-Baby in the road and goes to hide in some bushes.*)

"BRER RABBIT (meeting the Tar-Baby). Good-morning! Nice weather we're having."

Now go on from there, writing all the speeches.

11. THE GOLDEN WINDOWS

Beautiful windows, windows of gold,
Are the windows in my house,
I am told.

All day long the little boy worked hard, in field and barn and shed, for his people were poor farmers and could not pay a workman; but at sunset there came an hour that was all his own, for his father had given it to him. Then the boy would go up to the top of a hill and look across at another hill that rose some miles away. On this far hill stood a house with windows of clear gold and diamonds. They shone and blazed, so that it made the boy wink to look at them; but after a while the people in the house put up the shutters, as it seemed, and then it looked like a common farmhouse. The boy supposed they did this because it was supper-time; and then he would go into the house, and have his supper of bread and milk, and go to bed.

One day the boy's father called him and said, "You have been a good boy and have earned a holiday. Take this day for your own; but remember that God gave it, and try to learn some good thing."

The boy thanked his father and kissed his mother; then he put a piece of bread in his pocket and set out to find the house with the golden windows.

It was pleasant walking. His bare feet made marks in the white dust, and, when he looked back, the footprints seemed to be following him and making company for him. His shadow, too, kept beside him and would dance or run with him as he pleased; so it was very cheerful.

After a long time he came to a high green hill, and there was the house on the top; but it seemed that the shutters were up, for he could not see the golden windows. He came up to the house; and then he almost wept, for the windows were of glass, like any others, and there was no gold anywhere about them.

A woman came to the door, and looked kindly at the boy, and asked him what he wanted. "I saw your golden windows from our hilltop," he said, "and I came here to see them; but now they are only glass."

The woman shook her head and laughed. "We are poor farming people," she said, "and are not likely to have gold about our windows; but glass is better to see through."

She told the boy to sit down on the broad stone step at the door, and brought him a cup of milk and a cake, and bade him rest; then she called her daughter, a child of his own age, and nodded kindly at the two, and went back to her work.

The little girl was barefoot like himself and wore a brown cotton gown; but her hair was golden like the windows he had seen, and her eyes were blue like the sky at noon. She led the boy about the farm and showed him her black calf with the white star on its forehead; and he told her about his own calf with four white feet. Then, when they had become friends, the boy asked her about the golden windows. The little girl nodded and said she knew all about them, only he had mistaken the house.

"You have come quite the wrong way," she said. "Come with me, and I shall show you the house with the golden windows."

They went to a knoll that rose behind the farmhouse, and as they went, the little girl told him that the golden windows could be seen only at a certain hour, about sunset.

"Yes, I know that," said the boy.

When they reached the top of the knoll, the girl turned and pointed; and there on a hill far away stood a house with windows of clear gold and diamonds, just as he had seen them. And looking again, the boy saw that it was his own home.

Then he told the little girl that he must go; so he went back down the hill, and the little girl stood in the sunset light and watched him.

The way home was long, and it was dark before the boy reached his father's house; but the lamplight and firelight shone through the windows, making them almost as bright as he had seen them from the hilltop. When he opened the door, his mother came to kiss him, and his little sister ran to throw her arms about his neck, and his father looked up and smiled.

"Have you had a good day?" asked his mother. Yes, the boy had had a very good day.

"And have you learned anything?" asked his father.

"Yes," said the boy. "I have learned that our house has windows of gold and diamonds."

—Laura E. Richards.

Thinking about the Story

Everybody in the story of "The Golden Windows" is a kind person. Write down the names of all the people, and beside each name write one kind thing that that person did. Who is the most important person in the story? Why?

ANIMAL FRIENDS

Many of you have animal friends—dogs, cats, bunnies, and the like, and good friends they are. But wouldn't it be jolly to have friends among the wild animals? The stories and poems in this part of your Reader will help you to know how interesting such friends may be.

1. THE ANIMAL STORE

In this poem, a child thinks animal friends are worth at least a hundred dollars, "or maybe a little more." What animal friends would you buy with so much money?

If I had a hundred dollars to spend
  Or maybe a little more,
I'd hurry as fast as my legs would go
  Straight to the animal store.

I wouldn't say, "How much for this or that?
  What kind of dog is he?"
I'd buy as many as rolled an eye,
  Or wagged a tail at me!

I'd take the hound with the drooping ears
    That sits by himself alone;
Cockers and Cairns and wobbly pups
    For my very, very own.

I might buy a parrot all red and green,
    And the monkey I saw before,
If I had a hundred dollars to spend
    Or maybe a little more.

—RACHEL FIELD.

A PET STORE

After reading this poem, one class made a list of all the pets that they knew. They modelled them in plasticine, and set them up in a pet store.

On each pet they pinned a ticket with the pet's name. They were careful to spell each name correctly.

---

2. MERRIBOY

Here is a story that tells of good fun the children at school had with a squirrel, and the best of it is that the squirrel had good fun too.

The sun was breaking through the clouds when Merriboy, the squirrel, first poked his head over the garden fence. He scrambled up to the top of the highest post, and there he sat, his tail raised proudly and his head turning

hopefully from side to side in search of food.
But none was to be seen, and down to the ground
he ran again and began to look for nuts.

In a few moments the door of the class-room
opened, and Merriboy saw a small boy coming
toward him. In his hand the boy carried a
nut, which he threw to Merriboy. Then he
quickly crouched down close to the ground
to watch what the squirrel would do.

Soon another child came out from the class-
room, and then another, until the lawn was
dotted with children, each quietly waiting his
turn to throw the squirrel a nut.

Merriboy grew braver. As each nut was thrown to him, he snatched it and, sitting up saucily, slowly cracked the shell and broke the nut.

He was busy at this when, suddenly looking up, he found that all the children had gone. This was strange; where could they be? He had not seen them as they tiptoed quietly away.

When he had finished the last nut, he danced up to the class-room wall. Slowly he crept along it till he came to the door. Then he stopped and peeped shyly into the room.

There were the children! With heads bent busily over their work, they kept as quiet as mice, hoping that Merriboy would come in. Just inside on the mat, a nut was waiting for him. He hopped quickly to the spot, picked up the nut, and carried it to the flower-bed, where he hid it in a little hole.

This done, he turned and came back to the class-room, and there he found another nut waiting for him on the same spot. Five times he came back, and each time he carried away a prize.

But the sixth time there was no nut on the mat. He sniffed and sniffed and looked carefully all about him. There on the floor, a short distance away from him, he saw the treasure.

He moved a step or two forward, but before he reached the nut, a pencil fell with a sharp click to the floor, and away he ran to a safe place in the trees.

But Merriboy was brave, and he was soon on his way back to the garden once more.

Half-way across the lawn, he saw something strange lying on the grass. It had a bright red handle, and it ended in a mass of fur much thicker than his own. He jumped toward it, but just as he was about to snatch it, the wind ruffled the fur and frightened him away.

Backward and forward he went, hopping, creeping, and dancing, and shaking with fear. But he could not keep away; he must find out what the strange thing was. At last he sprang upon it. He thought it would turn upon him; but no, it lay without moving beneath his sharp little claws. It was only a mop, lying out in the sun to dry!

Again he went on his way, and once more he found the mat. A few feet farther on were the nuts. Inside the room everything was so quiet that you could have heard a pin drop, as each child watched, hardly daring to breathe. This time Merriboy ran straight to the nut, snatched it from the centre of the floor, and raced back to his home, shaking, but oh! so happy!

Days have passed since Merriboy first dared to face that roomful of boys and girls, and now he and his mate are daily visitors to the garden and the school. They sit together on the fence and chuckle happily, wash their faces and comb their tails, leap from branch to branch, and go bravely up to every strange thing they see on the lawn. Once Merriboy poked his head into a coffee-pot, but he did not like the taste.

The squirrels now come so often to the garden and the school-room that the children are looking forward to the day when Merriboy and his wife come with their babies to enter them as regular pupils in the primary class.

—*Adapted from* F. H. FINLAYSON.

FINDING WORDS

Find ten words that tell how Merriboy moved. When you have found them, write them down in a list. Beside each word write a sentence in which it is used. Your list will begin this way:

WORD	SENTENCE
poked	Merriboy poked his head over the fence.
scrambled	He scrambled up a post.

3. MY CHICKADEE GUESTS

Would it not be fun to have little birds eating breakfast with you, as they are with the man in the picture? Read the story, and find out how it may be done.

The air was cold, the snow was very deep, and many of the little wild birds were finding it hard to get their winter food. Some of them were dying because they could not find enough to eat. So I invited all the birds around my home to come and be my guests for the rest of the winter.

Just outside my study window I kept a tray filled with hemp, millet, and sunflower seeds, cracked nuts, and lumps of suet. There was another tray outside the bed-room window and still another outside the window

of the dining-room. If snow fell and covered
the food in the night, I brushed it off with
a whisk-broom early the next morning.

Many hungry birds came there every day
to feed. There were plump pine grossbeaks,
modest little red-polls, and one bright little
nut-hatch that seemed to think he owned the
whole garden.

Then there was a band of blue jays, that
always acted as if they were stealing the
food and were afraid of being caught at it.
They did not stay to enjoy a quiet meal, as
the grossbeaks did, but snatched all the food
they could carry and flew off with it. And
there was an old hairy woodpecker that came
for the suet. He spoke in a very loud voice,
and acted as if he did not want to be
interrupted.

The friendliest of all were the chickadees;
they always seemed as glad to see me as I
was to see them. They would come in a little
flock, and if I happened to be in the garden,
they would alight upon my hands and
shoulders, and almost ask me for something
to eat.

One morning when I awoke, I heard a

tapping at my window-pane, and there I saw
four little chickadees sitting in a row on the
window-sill, looking into the bed-room. Snow
that had fallen in the night covered all the
food in the trays, and it seemed as if they
were trying to make me hurry with breakfast.

I decided to invite them in to have breakfast
with me. I dressed quickly, went downstairs,
and pulled the breakfast table close to the
window. On the cloth I sprinkled broken
nuts, for chickadees are very fond of nuts.
Then I opened the window and whistled, and
in a few moments the birds came down to
the window-ledge.

For a minute or two they stood peeping
into the room and looking at the food on
the table. Then one after another of the little
birds flew in, and snatching up the bits of
nut, flew out into the garden to eat them.

Now this was very rude, for when you are
invited to breakfast, you are supposed to eat
at the table. So I thought I would give them
a lesson in politeness. First of all I swept
up the little bits of broken nuts, and then
with a needle and thread I stitched several
large pieces to the table-cloth.

When the chickadees came back, they tried to pick up the nuts, but they could not do it. This seemed to make them angry, for they flew out of the window and sat in the bushes near by, scolding me.

But scolding did not make them less hungry, so back they came. By this time I was eating my own breakfast—with an extra coat on, because the window was open. A chickadee alighted on the edge of the table, and stood looking at me from under his little black cap. I sat very still, and he hopped over to where half an English walnut was lying. He tried to pick it up, but the thread held fast.

Then he pecked at the kernel and looked up at me. I didn't move, and he tried it again. He seemed to like the taste of the nut, so, holding to the edge of the shell with his claws, he settled down and enjoyed himself.

The other chickadees looked in and saw him feeding there. One by one they followed him, until there were five chickadees eating breakfast with me. One of them came so near that his tail brushed my fingers. At first they were rather nervous, and would fly away if I moved my hands. But they always came back, and finding that there was nothing to be afraid of, they sat at the table, or on it, rather, until they had finished.

There have been many guests at my table since that day, but few have given me more pleasure, and certainly none have been more welcome, than those little hungry chickadees.

—Ernest Harold Baynes.

About Birds

In a book about birds, find pictures of all the birds that Mr. Baynes fed.

Draw a picture of each bird, making sure that it is the correct size and colour. Under each picture write a sentence or a phrase from the story that describes each bird.

There is a good song about chickadees. Part of it goes "Chickadee-dee, chickadee-dee." Perhaps a boy or a girl can find it for the class to sing.

One of Canada's most famous lovers of birds is Jack Miner. Write these five sentences about Jack Miner, but be sure you put the right parts together.

(1) Jack Miner, too,   by offering them food.
(2) He enjoys making friends visit his ponds.
(3) His lovely farm is   is a naturalist.
(4) Every year thousands of   at Kingsville, Ontario, near
    wild geese   Lake Erie.
(5) Mr. Miner tames birds   with birds and animals.

4. CHICKADEE

Hilda wrote this poem when she was eight years old.

The chickadee in the apple tree
Talks all the time very gently.
He makes me sleepy.
I rock away to the sea-lights.
Far off I hear him talking
The way smooth bright pebbles
Drop into water . . .
Chick-a-*dee-dee-dee* . . .

—HILDA CONKLING.

5. COBWEBS

Between me and the rising sun,
This way and that the cobwebs run;
Their myriad wavering lines of light
Dance up the hill and out of sight.

There is no land possesses half
So many lines of telegraph
As those the spider-elves have spun
Between me and the rising sun.

—E. L. M. KING.

6. KARI THE ELEPHANT

Kari the elephant was five months old when he was placed in the care of a little boy of India. The boy's name was Dhan Gopal Mukerji, and he was only nine years old when he received the elephant. Kari lived in a stable that was a kind of tent; the poles of the tent were trees whose tops had been cut off, and the roof was a thatched covering supported by the trees. It was necessary to use trees whose roots were solidly fixed in the ground, because, if Kari had bumped against an ordinary pole, he would have knocked it over, and then his whole stable would have come tumbling down. In the following story, Kari's young master tells what happened soon after the elephant arrived at his new home.

One of the first things Kari did was to save the life of a boy. Kari did not eat much, but he nevertheless needed forty pounds of twigs a day to chew and play with. Every day I used to take him to the river in the morning for his bath. He would lie down on the sand bank while I rubbed him with the clean sand of the river for an hour. After that he would lie in the water for a long time. On coming out, he would be shining like ebony, and he would squeal with pleasure as I rubbed water down his back. Then I would take him by the ear, because that is the easiest way to lead an elephant, and

leave him on the edge of the jungle while I went
into the forest to get some luscious twigs for his
dinner.

It was not an easy job, as you see, to get twigs
and saplings for Kari.   I had to climb all kinds
of trees to get the most delicate and tender twigs.
As he was very fond of the young branches of
the banian tree, which grows like a cathedral of
leaves and branches, I was gathering some, one
spring day in March, when I suddenly heard
Kari calling to me in the distance.   As he was
still very young, the call was more like that of
a baby than an elephant.   I thought somebody
was hurting him, so I came down from my
tree and ran very fast to the edge of the forest
where I had left him, but he was not there.

I looked all over, but I could not find him.
I went near the edge of the water, and I saw a
black something struggling above its surface.
Then it rose higher, and it was the trunk of my
elephant.   I thought he was drowning.   I was
helpless, because I could not jump into the water
and save his four hundred pounds.   But I saw
his back rise above the water, and the moment he
caught my eye he began to trumpet and struggle
up to the shore.   Then, still trumpeting, he

pushed me into the water, and as I fell into the stream, I saw a boy lying flat on the bottom of the river. He had not altogether touched bottom but was somewhat afloat. I came to the surface of the water to take my breath, and there Kari was standing, his feet planted into the sand bank, and his trunk stretched out like a hand waiting for mine. I dove down again and pulled the body of the drowning boy to the surface, but, not being a good swimmer, I could not swim ashore, and the slow current was already dragging me down. I clutched at reeds on the shore, but they broke, and the weight of the boy was tiring my hand. The other hand was already weak from swimming and clutching at the reeds.

Seeing us drift by in the current, Kari, who was usually so slow and heavy, suddenly darted down like a hawk and came halfway into the water, where I saw him stretch out his trunk again. I raised up my hand to catch it, and my hand slipped. I found myself going under the water again; but this time I found that the water was not very deep, so I sank to the bottom of the river and doubled my feet under me and then suddenly kicked the river bed and so shot upwards like an arrow, in spite of the fact that

I was holding the drowning boy with my hand.
As my body rose above the water, I felt a lasso
around my neck.   This frightened me; I thought
some water animal was going to swallow me.
Then I heard the squealing of Kari, and I knew
it was his trunk about my neck.   He pulled us
both ashore.

As the boy lay stretched on the ground, I
recognized the cowherd.   He had gone to bathe
in the river, had slipped too far out, and, not
knowing how to swim, had almost been drowned.
I put him flat on his face on the sand, and the
elephant put his trunk about his waist and lifted
it gently up and down, and then up again.
After doing this three or four times, the water
began to come out of the boy's mouth, and, not
knowing what else to do because his body was
cold, I slapped him very hard all over.   After
that I propped him up against the elephant's
leg.   Then the boy slowly came to.

In the meantime all his cows had wandered
away in different directions.   As I thought some
had gone into the jungle, where I was afraid
they might be eaten up by tigers, I sent Kari
to bring them back to the river bank.   But
Kari got lost himself; so when the cowherd had

recovered entirely, I went to look for his cows and my lost elephant. Where do you think I found him? He had gone right into the forest where I had left the saplings and the twigs and had buried his trunk into the heap and was eating the best of them, without any concern for the cows, the cowherd, or myself.

Kari was like a baby. He had to be trained to be good, and if you did not tell him when he was naughty, he was up to more mischief than ever.

But I could not punish him that day, because he had done his duty by saving the life of the boy.

—Dhan Gopal Mukerji.

Thinking about the Story

The boy talks about his baby elephant as if Kari were really a person. Here is an example: "I sent Kari to bring them (the cows) back to the river bank." Read the story again, and write down all the sentences and phrases you can find that speak of Kari in the same way.

Find out the following things about India:

(a) The name given to the people.
(b) The colours of the people.
(c) The kinds of wild animals that live there.
(d) Four facts about a jungle.
(e) Four peculiar things that some of the people do.

7. KING LION AND THE JACKALS

Jackals are wild animals that look very much like our dogs and are just as clever. There are many good stories told in India and Africa about jackals. Here is one in the form of a little play that you might act.

Characters:

KING LION - *Patrick*

FATHER JACKAL - *Neil*   MOTHER JACKAL - *Gai*

SCENE I

A great big jungle in Africa showing the opening of a big dark cave. This is the den of King Lion, who is seen looking out with a fierce expression.

KING LION. I am King of this great big jungle, gr-r-r-r-r. That will wake up the animals. Soon they will come along running this way and that. They will bump against one another, as they always do, and it will be easy to pick out the one I want for to-day's dinner. Gr-r-r-r-r. Gr-r-r-r-r.

(*There is silence in the jungle.*)

KING LION. What is this? Do the animals forget that I am King of the jungle?

I must see about it. If they won't come to me, I must go to them. Gr-r-r-r. No reply? But listen! I hear light footsteps.

(Father Jackal and Mother Jackal are seen in the distance. They have so often run past the opening of the cave that they are quite thin and very tired.)

MOTHER JACKAL. Oh, dear me! I feel sure our time has come; King Lion will catch us this time. We are the only ones left in the jungle. King Lion has eaten all the rest.

FATHER JACKAL. Cheer up! Cheer up! Let us run like the wind past the opening of the cave. Perhaps King Lion will not catch us.

(*They run like the wind, and the Lion is so big and heavy that he does not catch them this time.*)

SCENE II.   *The same.*

KING LION. Gr-r-r. This is the last time I will try this plan. What do I hear? Very light footsteps. Someone is coming.

(*Enter Father and Mother Jackal on their hind feet with their right and left fore feet touching, as if they were hand in hand.*)

MOTHER JACKAL. Oh, dear me! I feel sure our time has come. King Lion will certainly catch us this time.

FATHER JACKAL. Now, don't fret, Mother. Do as I tell you, and it will be all right.

(*They dance up to King Lion.*)

KING LION. You little rascals! Why did you not come before? Come here at once and let me eat you.

FATHER JACKAL. Yes, yes, King Lion. We were just coming to let you eat us, but another great big lion came and gave such a roar that we were afraid and ran away.

KING LION. How can that be? There is no other lion in the great big jungle.

MOTHER JACKAL. Indeed, oh, indeed, there *is* another lion. He is as much bigger than you as you are bigger than I.

KING LION (*standing up*). Take me to this lion, and I will eat him up. Then I will eat *you* up.

SCENE III

Another part of the jungle. A big well of water as clear as glass. King Lion stalks through the grass after the dancing Jackals.

FATHER JACKAL. Here is the big hole where the big, big lion lives. Look down, Your Majesty, and you will see him.

(*The Jackals move away as King Lion comes up to the well.*)

KING LION (*looking down into the well*). Another big lion sure enough, and a very fine one too. Gr-r-r-r. (*Shaking his mane and showing his teeth.*) Gr-r-r-r! You dare

to shake your mane and show your teeth at
me, do you? I will soon settle *you.*

(*The Lion jumps into the well and is
drowned.*)

FATHER AND MOTHER JACKAL (*dancing forward gaily, hand in hand*). King Lion is dead!
King Lion is dead !

—AN AFRICAN FOLK-TALE.

PRINTING SIGNS

When you act a play, you will help the people who listen
to it if you print signs to show what the different parts of
the scenery are meant to be. If a corner of the school-
room is to be the jungle, it should have a sign reading,
"A GREAT BIG JUNGLE." What other signs will you
need for this play?

---

8. BUNNY RABBIT

If you have ever watched the bunnies, you will enjoy
this poem. If you have never done so, try to find out where
there are wild rabbits, and by keeping very still you may
see them do everything mentioned in the poem.

Bunny creeps out and caresses his nose,
Combs out his ears with his fluttering toes,
    Blinks at the sun
    And commences to run
    With a skip and a hop
    And a flippety-flop,

Nibbling the clover wherever he goes;
But only when he is quite easy in mind
Does he button his little white tail down behind.

Bunny stops dead and stiffens each hair,
And his eyelids freeze in a terrified stare,
    And he pricks up his ears,
    For the sound that he hears
    Is a low muffled beat
    And a drumming of feet
And an ominous rub-a-dub-dubbing—but
    where?
He's off like the wind! He's off like the wind!
And his little white tail is unbuttoned behind.

               —AUTHOR UNKNOWN.

FINDING WORDS

Fill in the blanks in these sentences using *one* word for
each blank.
1. Bunny combs out his ...... with his ......
2. Bunny runs with a ...... and a ......
3. When he hears anything, he ...... up his ears.
4. Bunny likes to ...... the clover.
5. When he feels ......, he buttons his little white
   tail down ......
6. The rabbit heard the ...... of feet.
7. He ran like the ......
8. His little white tail was ...... behind.
9. The animal he heard coming was a ......

9. THE FIFTEEN ACRES

I cling and swing
On a branch, or sing
Through the cool, clear hush of Morning, O:
Or fling my wing
On the air, and bring
To sleepier birds a warning, O:
That the night's in flight,
And the sun's in sight,
And the dew is the grass adorning, O:
And the green leaves swing
As I sing, sing, sing,
Up by the river,
Down the dell,
To the little wee nest,
Where the big tree fell,
So early in the morning, O.

I flit and twit
In the sun for a bit
When his light so bright is shining, O:
Or sit and fit
My plumes, or knit
Straw plaits for the nest's nice lining, O:
And she with glee
Shows unto me

Underneath her wings reclining, O:
  And I sing that Peg
Has an egg, egg, egg,
    Up by the oat-field,
      Round the mill,
    Past the shadow,
      Down by the hill,
        So early in the morning, O.

  I stoop and swoop
  On the air, or loop
Through the trees, and then go soaring, O:
  To group with a troop
  On the gusty poop
While the wind behind is roaring, O:
  I skim and swim
  By a cloud's red rim
And up to the azure flooring, O:
  And my wide wings drip
  As I slip, slip, slip
    Down through the rain-drops,
      Back where Peg
    Broods in the nest
      On the little white egg,
    So early in the morning, O.

                    —JAMES STEPHENS.

10. MOTHER SPIDER

It could not have been a Canadian spider that "frightened Miss Muffet away," because our spiders are such fun to watch, spinning their webs and looking after their young.

It was a beautiful day in midsummer. The meadow was alive with busy little people moving about in the bright sunlight. A long line of ants came crawling down the path, carrying food to their home under the elm tree. Hopping along through the grass came an old toad, blinking in the warm sun.

Just a little higher up, the bees were buzzing as they flew from flower to flower. And above them all, in the clear blue sky, a robin was calling to his mate.

After a while Mother Spider came hurrying down the path, holding in her mouth a little white bag. Just then a big black beetle came rushing along the path. As Mother Spider

was going in front of Mr. Toad, the beetle
bumped against her and knocked the bag out
of her mouth.

In an instant Mother Spider pounced angrily
upon him. Though she was much smaller than
the beetle, she tumbled him over upon his back.
Then Mother Spider quickly took up her bag
and hurried away through the grass.

"Well, I never!" said Grasshopper Green,
who was playing see-saw on a blade of grass.

"I didn't want her bag," grumbled Mr.
Beetle, as he wriggled to his feet. "She needn't
have made such a fuss just because I stumbled
against her."

"She must have something very fine in that
bag," said Grasshopper Green. "She was so
frightened when she dropped it! I wonder!"

Not long after this, Grasshopper Green
started out for a little exercise. Just as he
reached the brook, he saw Mother Spider coming slowly toward him. She no longer carried
the little white bag, but he could see that she
had something on her back.

"Good-morning, neighbour," called Grasshopper Green. "Can I help you carry your
things?"

"Thank you very much," she said, "but they would fall off when you gave your great jumps."

"They!" cried Grasshopper Green in great surprise. And then, as he came nearer, he saw that the things on Mother Spider's back were tiny baby spiders.

"Aren't they beautiful children?" the proud mother asked. "I was so afraid that something would happen to my eggs, that I didn't once let go of the bag they were in, except when that stupid Mr. Beetle knocked it out of my mouth."

"Oho!" said Grasshopper Green. "So that was what frightened you, was it? The bag was full of eggs! And now you are carrying all those children on your back. Doesn't it tire you?"

"I don't mind the weight," said Mother Spider, "if only the children are well and safe. In a little while, you know, they will be able to run about by themselves. Then we shall be very happy here in the meadow grass. Oh, a family like this is well worth the trouble."

"Yes," said Grasshopper Green, "I have a dozen small boys of my own at home. And that reminds me that it is time to go home to breakfast. Good-bye, Neighbour Spider."

So home he went. And happy Mother Spider kept on her way to find a breakfast for the babies she loved so well.

—FRANCES BLISS GILLESPY.

WRITING SENTENCES

Tell in complete sentences: (a) the time of year; (b) what was in the bag; (c) why Mother Spider thought Mr. Beetle stupid; (d) what she carried on her back; (e) who offered to help her; (f) why she worked so hard.

---

11. THE BEAR AND THE BEES

Mr. Bruin discovered that bees are not on very friendly terms with bears. But then, Mr. Bruin was a robber bear, and could hardly expect to be treated as if he were a kind, friendly man. Have you ever found a gentlemanly bear in the fairy stories you have read?

Some bears, going out for a walk one day,
    Discovered in one of the trees
A hive full of honey, which smelt very fine,
    So they stopped to make friends with the
    bees.
The old bear bowed low, and said, "Brum, Brum,"
And the lady bee answered, "Hum, Hum, Hum."

"Madame Bee," said the bear to the fair little
      queen,
   "Yourself I am happy to meet!
I hope you'll invite me to share your feast,
   I'm exceedingly fond of what's sweet!"
And he tried to smile with his "Brum, Brum,
      Brum,"
But the bees all frowned with their "Hum, Hum,
      Hum."

Then the queen bee haughtily raised her head,
   As she sat on her leafy throne,
And said, "Mr. Bear, as you very well know,
   We bees prefer dining alone!"
Then the bear looked cross and grunted, "Brum,
      Brum,"
But the bees all smiled and applauded, "Hum,
      Hum."

"Heigh-ho, Mrs. Bee," said the angry bear,
   "You will please to bear this in mind,
There is nothing to hinder my taking it *all*
   Since you do not choose to be kind!"
And he stalked about with a loud "Brum, Brum,"
But the bees only laughed a low "Hum, Hum."

Then the bear began to climb up the tree,
  But the queen in her firmest tone,
Called up, "Mr. Bear, I must warn you now,
  You had better let *us* alone—
We are fully armed," but the bear sneered,
    "Brum!"
And the bees all savagely buzzed, "Hum, Hum!"

The soldier bees drew out their sharp, keen
    knives;
  While the little bees giggled with glee,
"Oh what a sore nose you will have, Mr. Bear,
  When you scramble down out of this tree!"

But the bear glared in rage while he growled,
     "Brum, Brum,"
And the sturdy young bees piped a saucy "Hum,
     Hum."

  Nearer he crept to the coveted prize;
     But that prize he was never to gain,
  For the knives pierced his nose, and his ears,
     and his eyes,
     Till he howled with the smart and the pain;
Down he went to the ground with a sad "Brum,
     Brum,"
While the bees in their triumph sang, "Hum,
     Hum, Hum!"

  "Now then, Mr. Bear," said the sage little
     queen,
     "If you would be healthy and wise,
  You must learn not to think quite so much
     of yourself,
     And all others you must not despise."
And the bear marched off with a sullen "Brum,
     Brum,"
While the busy bees buzzed with a pleasant
     "Hum, Hum."

                          —Author Unknown.

Bears and Bees

1. Read some bear stories in your library books, and try to find answers to these questions:

(*a*) What colours have different bears?

(*b*) Can you name the bear of each colour?

(*c*) In what parts of the world are bears found?

(*d*) What sort of food do they eat?

(*e*) Of what use are bears to man?

2. Study about bees in the same way, and answer these questions:

(*a*) What is a hive?

(*b*) Where do bees get their honey?

(*c*) Of what use are bees to flowers?

(*d*) Do bees really have a queen?

(*e*) How do they store their honey?

(*f*) What are "drones" and what happens to them?

---

12. OUR FRIEND MR. MUSKRAT

To study the animals we must stay very quiet while we catch them. One little move, and they are away!

We were off for the trout-pool. I sat at one end of the canoe and paddled, while Donald sat at the other, with his eyes wide open for any unusual sight. The sun had not been up long, and as we passed through the meadows, the air was still cool and sweet with the smell of wet grass and leaves. Wisps of mist curled

up from the river. Soon we came to a belt
of woods, and here the air was spicy with the
fragrance of fir, balsam, and cedar.

Presently we swung round a sharp bend in
the river, and all at once Donald held up a
warning hand. I stopped paddling and
looked ahead. Thirty yards or so in front of
us, there was something in the water. At
first sight it looked like the end of a small
sunken log or a stump; but when I looked at
it more closely, I could see that it was moving,
and that little ripples flowed back from it
on both sides.

"What is it?" asked Donald.

"Muskrat," said I softly; "it's going ashore
over there."

While we watched, it reached the bank, and
disappeared in a hole just at the edge of
the water. We had a glimpse of a thick,
fat body about a foot long, covered with
dark-brown hair, and a long, bare rat tail, and
then it was gone.

"What a wet, uncomfortable house he must
have!" said Donald.

"Oh, no, indeed! His house is dry and
warm, I'm sure," said I. "If you dug into

his hole, you would find that it slopes upward
from the water for a short distance, and then
at the end of a narrow passage widens into
quite a big room. There Mr. and Mrs.
Muskrat and their babies live warm and dry,
well above the reach of the highest spring
floods."

"But why is the muskrat's front door
under water?"

I laughed. "Oh, that is because he is less
likely to be disturbed by callers that he
doesn't care to see. They might get inside
and kill his little ones."

"But how does he get out in winter time
when the water is frozen?"

"He comes out under the ice, and feeds on reeds and roots whenever he wants to. He doesn't mind the cold water, for his thick fur sheds it, and keeps him warm and dry."

"I should like to get a closer look at one," said Donald.

"You would find that he looks much like a big rat. He has soft, thick brown fur and a long, rather flat, scaly tail, and he has webbed feet like a duck, to help him to swim easily. He is a harmless little animal."

"But why is he called a muskrat?"

"Because of his musky odour. I will paddle over to his hole, and then I think you will understand how he got his name."

I paddled over to the bank just beside the muskrat's hole. The mouth of the hole was about six inches wide, and was just under the water. On the muddy shore, and on the bottom of the river near the hole, were many half-eaten reeds and roots, which the muskrat and his family had brought home at various times.

"Not very tidy, is he?" said Donald. "When he has finished eating, he just throws the bones out at his front door."

"No," said I, "he doesn't care much for tidiness. What he is thinking of mostly is something to eat. Now," I went on, "just sniff a few times, and tell me if you understand how the muskrat got his name."

There was a very distinct musky odour in the air. It could not be mistaken.

"Yes," said Donald, "I understand. It certainly smells like musk here."

We paddled up the river to the trout-pool, and two hours later, on our way back, again neared the muskrat's hole.

"Let us go quietly now, and perhaps we may see Mr. Muskrat," said I.

So I stopped paddling, and let the canoe drift down stream with the current, giving my paddle a twist now and then to keep the canoe in the channel.

Presently we came in sight of the muskrat's hole. For a moment, though I looked closely, I could see nothing. Then I could make out the round, fat body of the muskrat, as he sat huddled up on the muddy bank near his hole. As I watched him, I could see that he moved slightly, and then I made out that he was gnawing a reed. We kept so still, and he was so busy with his lunch, that we got quite near before he saw us.

Then, all at once, there was a quick flash of brown, a plop in the water, and the muskrat had disappeared into his hole.

"Good-bye, Mr. Muskrat!" cried Donald. "We'll call again some other day."

—R. H. Bowles.

Making Notes

Read the story again, and as you read, write a sentence telling each thing that you learn about a muskrat. Try to have at least ten sentences.

What other water animals do we have in Canada?

---

13. WILD GOOSE

"Wild goose! Wild goose!
  How do you know the way,
From Southern California
  To the top of Hudson Bay?"
"Honk! Honk!" said the wild goose.
  "How should a body know?
I learned it in my geography,
  A hundred years ago."

—Isabel Bayne.

14. THE WOODPECKER

The woodpecker pecked out a little round hole
And made him a house in the telephone pole.

One day when I watched, he poked out his head,
And he had on a hood and a collar of red.

When the streams of rain pour out of the sky,
And the sparkles of lightning go flashing by,

And the big, big wheels of thunder roll,
He can snuggle back in the telephone pole.

—ELIZABETH MADOX ROBERTS.

DRAWING A PICTURE

This poem makes a very good picture. Before you draw the picture, be sure to find the right woodpecker in your class-room bird book.

---

15. POOR OLD ELEPHANT

An elephant to a circus went,
　　Poor old elephant!
And lived his life beneath a tent,
　　Poor old elephant!
Dreaming of the jungle cool,
　Juicy leaves and rippling pool.
　　Poor old elephant!

—L. FRANK BAUM.

16. LITTLE ORPHAN ROBIN

A child who has no father or mother is called an orphan. Everyone should be especially kind to orphans. Did you ever wonder who takes care of little orphaned birds?

Orphan Robin was very, very hungry, and there was no one to feed him. "What shall I do? What shall I do?" he squeaked. "I'm all alone. Where can Father and Mother be?"

Father and Mother Catbird and their three children were sitting in a low tree near by, and they heard Orphan Robin's cry.

"Do you hear that bird crying?" asked Father Catbird. "It must be Orphan Robin. If you can finish feeding our family, I'll find some worms for him."

"Yes, do," said Mother Catbird, "and I'll go over soon to see him."

"Oh, dear! Oh, dear! I'm hungry," Orphan Robin cried again.

"Yes, and he's lonely too," said Mrs. Catbird to herself. "Poor dear! He doesn't know that his father and mother will never come back to him again. He doesn't know, either, that Father Catbird perched on a branch near him all night long so that nothing could come to harm him."

While Mother Catbird was talking to herself, she was flying up and down from the nest to the garden, and from the garden to the nest, carrying worms to her hungry babies. Father Catbird was flying with her, but he was carrying his worms to little Orphan Robin, who now felt like singing.

"Where are Father and Mother?" asked little Orphan Robin, as Father Catbird gave him a large worm.

"They have gone away for a while," said Father Catbird, "and they left you in my care. Would you like to learn to sing and fly to-day?"

Father and Mother Robin had often been away for a little while, so Orphan Robin thought that this time they were only staying a bit longer, and he did not worry any more. Of course he would like a singing lesson. He told Father Catbird so, and they began at once.

"Meow," said Father Catbird. And little Orphan Robin tried and tried to say it like his teacher. But he couldn't say "Meow" at all.

"Try this, then," said Father Catbird, and

he sang a bluebird's song. Orphan Robin
tried and tried, but he couldn't sing a blue-
bird's song.

Then, very slowly, Father Catbird chirped
the notes of a robin.

"It's just like Father's voice," said little
Orphan Robin happily, as he chirped it after
Father Catbird.

"Now we'll have a flying lesson," said
Father Catbird.

At this, Orphan Robin perched on the edge
of the nest and shivered. He felt sure he
couldn't fly.

"If only Mother were here," he chirped, "I should not be afraid."

"I'm here," called Mrs. Catbird from her nest near by, making her voice like Mother Robin's. "Pretend that I am Mother and try to fly to me."

Mother Catbird's voice was so sweet and so comforting to Orphan Robin that almost before he knew it he was flying.

Mother and Father Catbird sang, "Well done, well done!" And in a very short time the little bird was both chirping and flying.

One day, when he was bigger, he flew over to the catbirds' nest and peeked in at the babies. They held up their little mouths so that he might put something into them, and he flew down to the ground and brought up a big, big worm for them.

"That was a happy thought," said Father Catbird. "You are lucky babies to have a robin for a big brother."

"Do you think that I could teach them how to fly?" Orphan Robin asked Father Catbird.

"Yes, of course," Father Catbird said. "You may give them their first lesson now."

Father and Mother Catbird stood happily to one side. Then they watched little Orphan Robin showing their babies how to flap their tiny wings, as Father Catbird had shown him such a short time before.

—ALICE WETHERELL.

A MODEL IN THREE SCENES

Use plasticine or paper to tell the story of the orphan robin. Let one part of the class make a model of the first scene, in which the catbirds adopt the little fellow. Let a second and a third group model the second and the third scenes. What are they about?

Think of good titles for each scene.

17. NATURE'S FRIEND

Say what you like,
  All things love me!
I pick no flowers—
  That wins the Bee.

The Summer's Moths
  Think my hand one—
To touch their wings—
  With Wind and Sun.

The garden Mouse
  Comes near to play;
Indeed, he turns
  His eyes away.

The Wren knows well
  I rob no nest;
When I look in,
  She still will rest.

The hedge stops Cows,
  Or they would come
After my voice
  Right to my home.

The Horse can tell,
  Straight from my lip,
My hand could not
  Hold any whip.

Say what you like,
  All things love me!
Horse, Cow, and Mouse,
  Bird, Moth, and Bee.

—W. H. DAVIES.

18. THE STARS AT NIGHT

Many children like to watch the stars as they come out one by one. Sometimes the children say a pretty little poem beginning:

> "Star light, star bright,
> First star I've seen to-night."

I've wondered, oh, so many times,
    What lights the stars at night,
And now, at last I've found it out!
    I know that I am right!

For only half an hour ago
    A band of bright fire-flies
Danced in and out among the trees,
    Searching for the skies!

And just a minute after that
    The stars shone clear and bright!
Of course, the fire-flies lighted them!
    Now tell me, am I right?

—Emeline Goodrow.

Making Verses

Which story about "how stars come out" do you like better, this one or the one on page 66. Try to turn the story on page 66 into a poem.

PLAY & LAUGHTER

Here is a section of your Reader full of fun. There are good stories and pretty poems about games and jokes. The first one is about a little girl who likes to play store.

1. GENERAL STORE

Some day I'm going to have a store
With a tinkly bell hung over the door,
With real glass cases and counters wide
And drawers all spilly with things inside.
There'll be a little of everything:
Bolts of calico; balls of string;
Jars of peppermint; tins of tea;
Pots and kettles and crockery;
Seeds in packets; scissors bright;
Kegs of sugar, brown and white;
Sarsaparilla for picnic lunches,
Bananas and rubber boots in bunches.
I'll fix the window and dust each shelf,

And take the money in all myself.
It will be my store, and I will say:
"What can I do for you to-day?"

—RACHEL FIELD.

PLAYING STORE

Many children play store in school, because playing store helps them with their number work, as well as with their reading and language. Most grocers would let children have samples with which to stock the store. It is fun, too, to make the play-money to pay for the things you buy. Of course, if you have a store in one corner of the room, you should have a house in another corner, because stores could not do business without houses.

Why is it called a general store? What is the tinkly bell for? Make a list of things mentioned in the poem which you can find in the picture. What is that thing at the end of the counter? Why is the top row in it different from the second row? What is in the little girl's pocket? Name four or five things not mentioned in the poem which you would like to have in *your* store.

2. JEANNIE'S KITTEN

"It never rains but it pours." Have you heard about that? And this time it rained—kittens.

The twins, Jeannie and Jock, were having a very happy summer at the farm, but one day Aunt Madge found Jeannie looking out of the window and sighing.

Aunt Madge put an arm around her. "What is the matter, dear?" she asked. "Do you feel sick?"

The little girl looked up. "No, not sick," she said, "but Mary Kent has the dearest little cuddly gray kitty, with a blue ribbon on its neck, and I wish I had one too."

Aunt Madge knew that Jeannie was feeling a little homesick, and she said, "Well, we must see if we can get you one. We really ought to have a cat in the house. I heard a mouse in the pantry last night, and old Barn Pussy never comes up to the house to catch mice at all."

So at the Women's Institute meeting that afternoon, Aunt Madge told the women about Jeannie's wish for a cat. "If anyone has a gray kitten that needs a home, we shall be glad to look after it," she said.

Nobody said anything at the time, but when Mrs. Brown reached home, she rang up Aunt Madge on the telephone. She said, "If the little girl wants a cat, we can spare one. Send her over for it to-night."

So after tea Jeannie and Jock went across the fields to Mrs. Brown's. Later in the evening they came home, each carrying a kitten. "Mrs. Lester called us in when we were passing and gave us the other one," they explained, and went to make a bed for their pets.

When Mrs. Murphy came in the morning to do the washing, she was carrying a covered basket and smiling brightly. "I heard that Jeannie wanted a kitten," she said, "so I just brought one for her and one for Jock."

As she opened the basket, two little gray furry balls tumbled out on the table and stood blinking at the light.

When the twins came home after school, each one was carrying a box. "More kitties, Auntie," laughed Jeannie. "Mrs. Burt sent one to school with Jimmie; and the other parcel was in the mail box with 'From a Friend' written on it."

Everyone in the place seemed to have heard that Jeannie wanted a kitten. Even the neighbourhood cats, themselves, must have heard a whisper about Jeannie's wish, because in the next few days Jeannie and Jock found three cats sitting near the front gate. And one of them had brought a kitten.

Grandad had been away for a few days, and on his return the twins ran to meet him to tell him the cat joke. "Wait a minute, Twinnies," he said, "I brought a surprise from the city for you."

He opened up a pretty wicker hamper and

there, curled up on a dark blue cushion, lay the loveliest white Persian kitten! The twins shouted with delight and laughed till Grandad thought they would hurt themselves.

They kept the white pussy in the house, and put the six gray kittens and the three gray cats in an empty box-stall in the barn. One night the door of the stall was left open, and next day there was not a cat to be seen except old Barn Pussy, who sat there washing her face and looking quite contented.

That evening after school Uncle John called the children to the barn. "Come and I'll show you why old Barn Pussy chased all the other pussies home," he said.

The twins ran to look, and there, curled up on the hay under the stairs, was old Barn Pussy with six tiny wee kittens!

Grandad laughed about the cat story for weeks afterwards.

"At your next Institute meeting, Madge," he said, "I wish you would say that we need a new cow. Then we shall see if the good folk will make it rain cattle instead of cats."

—Elsie M. Campbell.

3. THE OWL AND THE PUSSY-CAT

"I have never heard such nonsense!" Has anyone
ever said that to you? Perhaps you will say it, too, when
you have read the poem. But isn't it fun?

The Owl and the Pussy-Cat went to sea
   In a beautiful pea-green boat;
They took some honey, and plenty of money
   Wrapped up in a five-pound note.
The Owl looked up to the stars above,
   And sang to a small guitar,
"O lovely Pussy! O Pussy, my love,
   What a beautiful Pussy you are—
          You are,
   What a beautiful Pussy you are!"

Pussy said to the Owl, "You elegant fowl,
   How wonderfully sweet you sing!
Oh! let us be married; too long we have tarried:
   But what shall we do for a ring?"
They sailed away for a year and a day
   To the land where the bong-tree grows;
And there in a wood, a Piggy-wig stood,
   With a ring at the end of his nose—
          His nose,
   With a ring at the end of his nose.

"Dear Pig, are you willing to sell for one shilling
  Your ring?"   Said the Piggy, "I will."
So they took it away, and were married next
  day
  By the turkey who lives on the hill.
They dined upon mince and slices of quince,
  Which they ate with a runcible spoon;
And hand in hand, on the edge of the sand,
  They danced by the light of the moon—
          The moon,
  They danced by the light of the moon.

                        —EDWARD LEAR.

A BOOK OF NONSENSE

Edward Lear was a big man with bushy whiskers, who
wrote a whole *Book of Nonsense*. Ask one of the pupils
to borrow it from the library so that the boys and girls
may read it to one another.

A girl said that "runcible" is a funcible word.

---

4. A RIDDLE

The man in the wilderness asked of me
How many strawberries grew in the sea.
I answered him, as I thought good,
As many red herrings as grew in the wood.

                        —AUTHOR UNKNOWN.

5. THE QUAKER BONNETS

Snowdrops, sweet-peas, and baby's-breath: what beautiful names the flowers have! Have you ever wondered how their names came to them? The story tells us about sweet-peas.

Lucy Jane was helping Mother to arrange sweet-peas and baby's-breath for the dinner-table. There were pinks and blues and mauves among the sweet-peas; yes, and the lovely creamy white that the catalogue called Ivory Queen.

Lucy Jane loved flowers, and most of all those that came from her own part of the garden. She was always curious about their names, and asked many questions as to why these names had been given to them.

"Where did the sweet-peas get their names, Mother?" she asked, as she selected a beautiful white with pink edges to go next to a salmon-pink.

"I am not at all sure," answered Mother, "but I will tell you the story that was told to me when I was a girl.

"Once there were three little Quaker maids, Prudence, Priscilla, and Patience. Like all the Quaker maids, they were always dressed very plainly, in soft gray dresses and quaint, gray bonnets.

"They were happy little girls, until a cousin of Priscilla's, who lived in a near-by city, and who was not a Quakeress, came to visit them. She brought many lovely clothes with her, not gray at all, but pink and blue, and even red.

"The little Quaker maids did not wish for

dresses like those of their cousin, but they did admire the gay little hats that had almost all the colours of the rainbow upon them.

"After the visitor had gone back home, the three little girls put their heads together, and decided to do something very bold. They would buy some coloured cloth, and make some gay bonnets instead of the gray ones they had always worn. So off they went to the shop.

"Priscilla bought a lovely pink, Prudence a bright blue, while Patience said she had always longed for white, so a creamy white she chose. At home they made up the gay bonnets just like their own little gray ones, and they were very pretty indeed.

"The next Sunday, which the Quakers call First Day, they went as usual to the meeting house, which stood just beside a lovely green wood. As the three little girls entered, everyone looked very hard at them, for such a thing had never happened before. Even the elders looked shocked.

"The little girls sat down and waited with lowered eyes for someone to speak. Suddenly a wind seemed to fill the whole room. It blew harder, and lifting the little bonnets right off the little heads, carried them out through the window and away, beyond the lovely green wood.

"The girls never saw the bonnets again, but the next summer, beyond the same wood, flowers like these, pink and blue and creamy white, were growing. They looked so much like the little Quaker bonnets that people began calling them Sweet P's, after the three little maids whose names began with P."

"What a lovely story!" cried Lucy Jane, as she put a rose pink, a bright blue, and a creamy white flower side by side. "Here they are, and I seem to see the little Quaker faces inside them."

—Martha Lindley Hall.

Finding Similar Stories

The story of "The Quaker Bonnets" pretends to tell us how sweet-peas came to be. In your Reader you have studied other stories and poems that tell how things came to be.

Look back through the book, and find the names of all such stories. Then write down the titles, one under the other, and beside each title write the name of the thing that the story tries to explain.

6. THE CROWN

Boys often wish they were princes. Do you think a prince ever wishes he were just a boy?

A little Prince
In cloth-of-gold,
The day that he
Was six years old,
Said, "I will go
Into the town
And show the people
There my crown,"
And with his treasure
In his hands
Went dancing through
His father's lands.

He chanced to see,
As he skipped by,
A meadow where
The lambkins lie,
And all the grass
Beneath their feet
Was strewn with daisies
Small and sweet.

Another boy
With gipsy hair
Beneath a tree
Was watching there
To see that not
A lambkin strayed;
And on a whistle-
Pipe he played.

The little Prince
Had never heard
So sweet a sound,
For, like a bird,
Its reedy notes
So clear and shrill
Went echoing
Across the hill.
He nods his head
And seems to smile,
His fingers moving
All the while.
His hands are brown.
His dark eyes seem
As careless as
A sunlit stream.

The little Prince
In wonder stands,
His gold crown shining
In his hands.

The King sits in
His pillared halls,
And for the little
Prince he calls.
And when the sun
Goes flaming down,
The boy returns
Without a crown,
But skipping gaily
Up the hill,
Piping music
Sweetly shrill,
And stands before
His father there,
A chain of daisies
On his hair.
While in the fields
Beneath the tree
The shepherd stands,
Amazed to see
His shepherd boy

Come stepping down
In holland smock
And golden crown.

—JOAN AGNEW.

MAKING UP A PLAY

Several classes have made beautiful plays out of the poem about the little prince who traded clothes with the shepherd boy. They made up their own speeches and wrote them down just as you did for "The Tar-Baby."

---

7. MAY

Merry, rollicking, frolicking May
Into the woods came skipping one day.
She teased the brook till he laughed outright
And gurgled and scolded with all his might.
She chirped to the birds and bade them sing
A chorus of welcome to Lady Spring.
And the bees and butterflies she set
To waking the flowers that were sleeping yet.
She shook the trees till the buds looked out
To see what the trouble was all about,
And nothing in Nature escaped that day
The touch of the life-giving, bright, young May.

—GEORGE MACDONALD.

8. THE LAUGHING DRAGON

When you look at the pictures, you will feel like laughing. And as you read the story you *will* laugh, for this is a very funny dragon story.

I

There was once a king who had three sons. He had also a very loud voice. His voice was *very* loud. It was so loud that when he spoke everyone jumped. So they called the country he ruled over by the name of Jumpy.

But one day the King spoke in a very low voice indeed. And all the people ran about and said, "The King is going to die."

He *was* going to die, and he *did* die. But before he died, he called his three sons to his bedside. He gave one half of Jumpy to the eldest son; and he gave the other half to the second son. Then he said to the third, "You shall have five dollars and five cents, and you shall have the small bag in my private box."

In due time the third son got his five dollars and five cents, and put it safely away into his purse. Then he got the bag from the King's private box. It was a small bag made of kid and was tied with a string.

The third son, whose name, by the way, was Tumpy, untied the string and looked into the bag. Then he looked again. It had nothing in it but a very queer smell. Tumpy sniffed, and then he sneezed. Then he laughed, and laughed, and laughed again, without in the least knowing what he was laughing at.

"I shall never stop laughing," he said to himself. But he did, after half an hour and two minutes exactly. Then he smiled for three minutes and a half.

After that he looked very happy; and he kept on looking so very happy that his friends called him Happy Tumpy, or H.T. for short.

II

Next day H.T. set out to seek his fortune. He had tied up the bag again and put it into the very middle of his bundle.

His mother gave him some bread and a piece of cheese, two apples, and a banana. Then he set out with a happy face. He whistled as he went along with his bundle on a stick over his shoulder.

After a time he was tired and sat down on a large mile-stone. As he was eating an apple, a black cat came along. It rubbed its side against the large stone, and H.T. stroked its head.

Then it sniffed at the bundle that lay on the grass. Next it sneezed, and then it began to laugh. It looked so funny that H.T. began to laugh too.

"You must come with me, puss," said H.T. The cat was now smiling broadly. It looked up at H.T., and he fed it. Then they went on side by side.

By and by H.T. and the cat came to a town, where they met a tall, thin man.

"Hello," he said, and H.T. said the same.

"Where are you going?" asked the man.

"To seek my fortune," said H.T.

"I would give a small fortune to the man who could make me laugh."

"Why?" said H.T.

"Because I want to be fat," said the man, "and people always say, 'Laugh and grow fat.'"

"How much will you give?" said H.T.

"Oh, six dollars and five cents anyhow," said the man.

H.T. put down his bundle and took out his bag. He held it up near the man's face and untied the string. The man sniffed, and then he sneezed. Then he laughed for half an hour and two minutes. Next he smiled for three minutes and a half.

By that time he was quite fat. So he paid H.T. six dollars and five cents. Then he went on his way with a smile and a wave of the hand.

"If I go on like this, I shall soon make my fortune," said H.T. He tied up his bag and went on again. The black cat walked after him with a smile on its face that never came off.

III

After an hour the two companions came to another town. There were many men in the street, but no women, or boys, or girls. The men looked very much afraid. H.T. went up to one of them. "Why do you look so much afraid?" he asked politely.

"You will look afraid, too, very soon," said the man. "The great dragon is coming

again. It comes to the town each day, and
takes a man and a cheese. In ten minutes
it will be here."

"Why don't you fight it?" asked H.T.

"It is too big and fierce," replied the man.
"If any man could kill it, he would make his
fortune."

"How is that?" said H.T. "Well," said
the man, "the King would give him a bag of
gold and make the princess marry him."

All at once H.T. heard a loud shout.

"The dragon is coming!" called a man
who wore a butcher's apron. Then he ran
into his shop, banged the door, and threw a
large piece of meat out through the window.
There was now nothing in the street but
H.T., the cat, and the piece of meat.

H.T. did not run away, not even when he
saw the huge dragon come lumbering up the
street on all fours. It crept along and
turned its head this way and that. Its face
was terrible to look at. Fire came out of its
nose when it breathed out. And three of the
houses began to burn.

Then the dragon came to the meat. It
sniffed it and stopped to eat it. That gave

H.T. plenty of time to carry out his plan.

He took out his bag and untied the string. Then he threw it down before the dragon. On it came, blowing more fire from its nostrils. Soon the butcher's shop was burning. There was a noise like the noise from an oven when the meat is roasting.

The dragon still came on. When it got up to the bag, it stopped. It sniffed. Then it sneezed so hard that two houses fell down flat. Next it began to laugh, and the noise was so loud that the church steeple fell into the street.

Of course the dragon had stopped to laugh. It sat up on its hind legs and held its sides with its fore-paws. Then it began to smile. And a dragon's smile, you must understand, is about six feet wide!

The dragon looked so jolly that H.T. did not feel afraid of it any more—not in the least. He went up to it and took one of its fore-paws under his arm. The cat jumped on the dragon's head. And Tumpy and the dragon and the cat all went along the street on their way to the king's palace as jolly as sand-boys.

IV

A woman popped her head out of a high window. "Take the first turn to the right," she said, "and the second to the left. Then you will come to the King's royal palace. You cannot miss it."

"Thank you very much," said H.T.; and he and the dragon and the cat smiled up at her. H.T. waved his hand. The dragon waved its other fore-paw. And the cat waved its tail.

So they went on—down one street and then another. At last they came to a big, open, green space in which stood a great palace. It had a wall round it with four large gates in it. At each gate there was a sentry box. But not one sentry could be seen.

H.T., with his friend the dragon, came smiling up to one of the gates. Above the gate H.T. saw someone peeping over the wall. "He wears a crown," he said to the dragon, "so it must be the King." The dragon kept on smiling.

"Hello!" cried the King. "What do *you* want?"

"Hello!" cried H.T. "I want the bag of gold and the princess."

"But you have not killed the dragon," said the King.

"I should think not," said H.T. "Why, he is my friend. He is my very dear friend. He will not do any harm now. Look at him."

The King stood up and put his crown straight. In his fright it had fallen over one eye. The dragon went on smiling in a sleepy kind of way. There was no fire in his nose now.

"But," said the King, "how do I know he will not begin to kill people again?"

"Well," said H.T., "we will make a big
kennel for him and give him a silver chain.
Each day I will give him a sniff from my
empty bag.   Then he will be happy all
day and go to sleep every night."

"Very well," said the King.   "Here is the
bag of gold.   You will find the princess
in the laundry.   She always irons my collars.
And you can have my crown as well.   It
is very hard and heavy.   I do not want to
be King any more.   I only want to sit by
the fire and have a pipe and play the gram-
ophone or the radio."

So he threw his crown down from the
wall.   The dragon caught it on its tail and
put it on H.T.'s head.   Then H.T. went to
the laundry and married the princess right
away.

And the dragon lived happily ever after; and
so did the cat; and so did everybody else, at
least until they died.

I ought to tell you that King H.T. used the
bag all his life to keep the dragon laughing.   The King died at the age of three hundred
and one years, one month, a week, and two
days.

The very next day after King H.T. died, the dragon took a very hard sniff at the bag. And he laughed so much that he *died* of laughing.

So they gave the bag to the dentist. And when anyone had to have a tooth out, he took a sniff. Then he laughed so much that he did not feel any pain. And when the tooth was out, he was happy ever after, or at least until the next time that he ate too many candies.

—RICHARD WILSON.

MURALS

The story of "The Laughing Dragon" is one of the best stories in the book from which to make murals. (What are *murals*?)

First, find out how many scenes the class will need to draw in order to tell the whole story by pictures.

Then ask your teacher to divide the class into as many groups as there are scenes. Each group should draw at least one scene. Try not to copy any of the pictures that the artist has drawn for you.

Happy hearts and happy faces
Happy play in grassy places,
That was how in ancient ages
Children grew to kings and sages.

9. THE DUEL

Why the gingham dog and the calico cat should have hated each other, nobody, I suppose, ever knew. And now, nobody ever can know. Poor dog! Poor cat!

The gingham dog and the calico cat
Side by side on the table sat;
  'Twas half-past twelve, and (what do you
    think?)
  Nor one nor t'other had slept a wink!
  The old Dutch clock and the Chinese plate
  Appeared to know as sure as fate
There was going to be a terrible spat.
    (*I wasn't there; I simply state*
    What was told to me by the Chinese plate!)

The gingham dog went, "Bow-wow-wow!"
And the calico cat replied, "Mee-ow!"
  The air was littered, an hour or so,
  With bits of gingham and calico;
  While the old Dutch clock in the chimney-
    place
  Up with its hands before its face.
For it always dreaded a family row!
    (*Now mind: I'm telling you*
    What the old Dutch clock declares is true!)

The Chinese plate looked very blue,
And wailed, "Oh, dear, what shall we do?"
  But the gingham dog and the calico cat
  Wallowed this way and tumbled that,
  Employing every tooth and claw
  In the awfullest way you ever saw;
And oh, how the gingham and calico flew!
    (Don't fancy I exaggerate—
    I got my news from the Chinese plate!)

Next morning, where the two had sat
They found no trace of dog or cat;
  And some folks think unto this day
  That burglars stole that pair away!
  But the truth about the cat and pup
  Is this: they ate each other up!
Now, what do you really think of that?
    (The old Dutch clock it told me so,
    And that is how I came to know.)

                       —Eugene Field.

A Tapping Poem

  The class will find it interesting to read this poem together, tapping lightly with their toes while they read:
      The gingham dog and the calico cat
        tap   tap   tap   tap
  There are two or three places in each verse where you will have to take a rest and tap without reading.

10. THE RABBIT'S TRICK

The elephant and the whale, because they are so big, thought they could rule the animals. But the rabbit was too clever for them, just as he was too clever for the fox in the story on page 121.

One day Brother Rabbit was running along the sea-shore when he saw a Whale and an Elephant talking together. He crouched down and listened to what they were saying, and this is what he heard:

"You are the biggest animal on the land, Brother Elephant," said the Whale, "and I am the biggest one in the sea; if we work together, we can rule all the animals and do just as we please."

"Excellent," said the Elephant; "that just suits me; we'll do it."

The Rabbit smiled. "They will not rule me," he said. Off he ran and soon came back with a long, strong rope and a big drum. He hid the drum some distance away in the bushes. Then he ran along the shore till he met the Whale.

"Brother Whale," said he, "will you do me a favour? My cow is stuck in the mud away back in the bushes, and I am not strong enough to pull her out. May I ask you to help me?"

"Certainly," said the Whale, "I shall be glad to assist you."

"Then," said the Rabbit, "let me tie this end of my rope round you, and I shall run back into the bushes and tie the other end round my cow, and when I have done that, I shall beat on my drum. You will have to pull hard, for the cow is down deep in the mud."

"Pshaw!" said the Whale, "I will pull her out even if she is covered to the tips of her horns."

The Rabbit tied the rope to the Whale and ran off as fast as he could to the place where the Elephant was feeding.

"Dear Mr. Elephant," said he, "will you do me a kindness?"

"What do you want?" asked the Elephant.

"My cow is stuck in the mud some distance down on the shore, and I am not strong enough to pull her out. May I ask you to help me?"

"Why, of course," said the Elephant.

"Then," said the Rabbit, "let me tie one end of this rope to your trunk and the other to my cow, and when I have done this, I shall beat on my big drum. When you hear that, pull with all your might, for the cow is a large one."

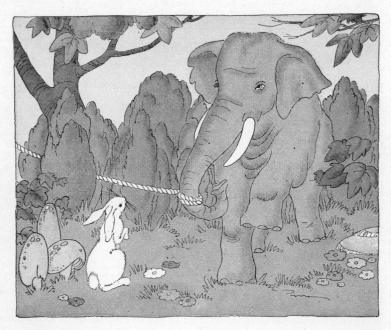

"Nonsense," said the Elephant. "I could pull
a dozen cows."

"I feel sure of that," said the Rabbit, "only
do not pull too hard at first."

When he had tied the rope about the Elephant's trunk, he ran back to a little hill in
the bushes, where he could see what was about
to happen, and began to beat the drum.

Whale and Elephant began at once to pull.

"That is a remarkably heavy cow," said
the Elephant, "but out she must come."

"Well, well!" said the Whale, "that cow must be far down in the mud."

Hard as the Whale pulled, the Elephant pulled harder, for he had a more solid footing. Presently the Whale found himself sliding toward the shore. As he neared the land, he became so angry at the thought of that cow, that he plunged violently head foremost to the bottom. This jerked the Elephant off his feet, and before he could recover himself, he was pulled right down to the edge of the water. He was furious.

Just then the Whale ceased pulling for an instant, and the Elephant leaped back with a jerk that brought the Whale to the surface of the water.

"What do you suppose you are pulling on?" shouted the Whale.

"What are you doing with that rope?" roared the Elephant.

"I will teach you to play cow," said the Elephant.

"And I will show you how to trick me," said the Whale.

Each put forth all his strength, but the rope broke, and heels over head tumbled Elephant and Whale.   This made them both so ashamed and angry that it broke up the bargain between them.

And that little Rabbit in the bushes declared that he had never had such fun in his life.

—Author Unknown.

Finding the Meanings of Words

Write the words below, one under the other, and beside each word write a word or a phrase that means the same thing:

crouched　distance　solid　recover　surface
excellent　remarkably　violently　instant　bargain

---

11. ONE, TWO, THREE

Most children have played Hide-and-Go-Seek, but not the way this little boy and the old, old lady played it.

It was an old, old, old, old lady,
　And a boy who was half-past three;
And the way that they played together
　Was beautiful to see.

She couldn't go running and jumping,
　And the boy, no more could he,
For he was a thin little fellow,
　With a thin little twisted knee.

They sat in the yellow sunlight,
  Out under the maple tree;
And the game that they played, I'll tell you,
  Just as it was told to me.

It was Hide-and-Go-Seek they were playing,
  Though you'd never have known it to be,
With an old, old, old, old lady
  And a boy with a twisted knee.

The boy would bend his face down
  On his one little sound right knee,
And he'd guess where she was hiding
  In guesses One, Two, Three.

"You are in the china closet!"
  He would cry, and laugh with glee.
It wasn't the china closet;
  But he still had Two and Three.

"You are up in Papa's big bed-room
  In the chest with the queer old key!"
And she said, "You are warm and warmer,
  But you're not quite right," said she.

"It can't be the little cupboard
  Where Mamma's things used to be,

So it must be the clothes-press, Gran'ma,"
   And he found her with his Three.

Then she covered her face with her fingers,
   That were wrinkled and white and wee,
And she guessed where the boy was hiding
   With a One, and a Two, and a Three.

And they never stirred from their places
   Right under the maple tree,
This old, old, old, old lady
   And the boy with the lame little knee,
This dear, dear, dear, dear lady
   And the boy that was half-past three.

—Henry Cuyler Bunner.

Thinking about the Poem

"One, Two, Three" has been loved by children for many
years. From the following sentences write down those
that give good reasons for children liking it:

   1. They feel sorry for the little boy.
   2. The poem has a story in it.
   3. It says "One, two, three."
   4. It tells of a new way to play hide-and-go-seek.
   5. The poem makes a pretty picture.
   6. The little boy's mother is kind to him.
   7. The maple leaf is "our emblem dear."
   8. The old, old, old, old lady is kind.
   9. The little boy likes his grandmother.
   10. They are happy together.

12. PETERKIN SPRAY

The full name of this poem is "The Wonderful Fishing of Peterkin Spray." Very wonderful, indeed, it must have been, and the selling of the fish was wonderful, too. For Peterkin sailed away into the sky to find his customers. Many boys and girls have thought they would like to sail among the stars, look through the golden windows of the sun, the silver windows of the moon, and even take a peek to see what really is inside the Dipper. But boys and girls can only wish; Peterkin really did it.

A fisherman bold was Peterkin Spray,
And he sailed, and he sailed, and he sailed away;
And when he got there, he embarked once more,
Down the path that leads to the Sun's back door.
"Ho, Ho," said the Sun, "here is Fisherman
    Spray,
But the cook doesn't need any salmon to-day."

"Too bad, Mr. Sun," said Peterkin Spray,
And he sailed, and he sailed, and he sailed away;
But the wind was so light that 'twas half past
    eight
When he called his wares at the Moon-man's
    gate.
"Fresh fish!" he cried, but the Moon-man said,
"I never eat fish when I'm going to bed."

"What a fussy old Moon!" sighed Peterkin Spray,
And he sailed, and he sailed, and he sailed away;
And when he got there, he exclaimed, "My Stars!
I had almost forgotten to call on Mars."
"Fine fish," cried Mars, and he smacked his lips,
"Charge a dozen or so to my next eclipse!"

"O dear, O dear!" sighed Peterkin Spray,
And he sailed, and he sailed, and he sailed away;
And when he got there, he declared, "I wish
I never, never had learned to fish.
For some won't buy, and others won't pay,
And I'm tired, and tired of sailing away!"

"I know what I'll do!" said Peterkin Spray,
And he turned his boat down the Milky Way.
He opened the Dipper (yes, honest, he did!),
He popped in his cargo, and slapped down the
    lid.
"Here's a kettle of fish!" laughed Peterkin Spray.
And he sailed, and he sailed, and he sailed away.

—Isabel Ecclestone Mackay.

Choosing a Way to Read

You have read so many poems together that you will
have no trouble in finding the way to read "Peterkin Spray"
as a choir.   In reading it together, make use of the speeches
and the line that is repeated in each verse.

OTHER LANDS THAN OURS

In this part of your book you will read about boys and girls who live in far countries. Perhaps you will find that they are very much like boys and girls who live in our country.

1. FOREIGN CHILDREN

Little Indian, Sioux, or Crow,
Little frosty Eskimo,
Little Turk or Japanee,
O! don't you wish that you were me?

You have seen the scarlet trees
And the lions over seas;
You have eaten ostrich eggs,
And turned the turtles off their legs.

Such a life is very fine,
But it's not so nice as mine;

You must often, as you trod,
Have wearied *not* to be abroad.

You have curious things to eat,
I am fed on proper meat;
You must dwell beyond the foam,
But I am safe and live at home.

Little Indian, Sioux, or Crow,
Little frosty Eskimo,
Little Turk or Japanee,
O ! don't you wish that you were me?

—Robert Louis Stevenson.

Studying Foreign Children

This part of the book tells about seven different children who live in other lands than ours. One of the most interesting things to do with these stories and poems, from page 215 to page 242, is to make dolls, and dress them as the children of these lands might be dressed.

A very easy kind of doll may be made from stove-pipe wire. What would you use to make the head?

It is still more interesting, after the dolls are made, to make little houses, and put the dolls in the gardens. Which of the people in "other lands than ours" might not have a garden?

To help you with your work, study the pictures in this part of your Reader. You should also look for more help in books in the library. Try to make the houses, the dresses, and the gardens just as they would be in the other land.

2. HEIDI

Heidi is a beautiful little Swiss girl who lives in those great mountains of Switzerland called the Alps. A whole book has been written about her, a book which all children love to read. When you read the following story about Heidi, you should say her name as if it were "High-dee."

High on the Alps there lived an old man all alone. His hut stood on a jutting cliff, overlooking the beautiful valley below. Back of the hut grew tall pine trees, large and old, with thick, rough branches. Beyond the trees, the mountains rose up to gray, rocky peaks that towered into the sky.

The old man had placed a bench on the side of his hut toward the valley. Here he sat resting one day, when suddenly he saw a little girl running toward him.

"Good-day, Grandfather," she said. "I am Heidi, and I have come to stay with you. My aunt has shown me the way up the mountain."

"Well, well, what does this mean?" said the old man. He held out his hand to the little girl and gave her a long look from under his bushy eyebrows. The child stood before him waiting, with her hands folded behind her back.

"What would you like to do?" asked the grandfather kindly.

"I should like to go into the hut and see what you have there," answered the little girl.

"Take up your bundle then and come!"

Heidi followed her grandfather into the little house. There was a bed in the corner, a table, one chair, a door that opened into a closet, and a ladder which led to the loft.

Heidi looked carefully about the room. Her bright eyes seemed to see everything at a glance.

"Where shall I sleep, Grandfather?" she asked.

"Where you like," was his answer.

This pleased the child, and she ran to the ladder. Up climbed Heidi and found herself in a little room half filled with fragrant hay. Through a small, round window she could see for miles across the valley below.

"I shall sleep here," she cried. "Oh, it is beautiful. Come up, Grandfather, and see how beautiful it is. How I wish it were night so that I could lie down!" she exclaimed.

"We had better have something to eat first," said her grandfather. "What do you say?"

All at once Heidi felt very hungry, and she answered heartily, "I think so, too."

Soon a bright fire was burning in the open fireplace, and the kettle boiled merrily. The old man put a piece of cheese on a long iron fork, and held it over the coals until it was a golden yellow on all sides. Heidi ran to the cupboard, where she had seen the bread and the dishes. When her grandfather came with the toasted cheese and the cup of tea, the table was nicely laid with the loaf of bread in the middle.

"You know what to do without being told," said the old man, "and that is good." He filled a bowl with goat's milk for Heidi and spread her bread thickly with hot cheese. The child grasped the bowl and drank without stopping.

"I never tasted such good milk," she said.

"Then you must have more," and the grandfather filled the little bowl to the brim.

Suddenly a whistle sounded, and down from the mountains came the goats with Peter, the goatherd. Two beautiful, slender goats, one white and one brown, came running out of the flock. They went to the old man and licked his hands. Heidi stroked them gently.

"Are they ours, Grandfather?" she asked. "Will they go into our shed? Will they always stay with us? May I play with them?"

"Yes, yes, child," answered her grandfather, as he fed them with salt. "Now, Heidi," he added, "get your bowl, and I will fill it with fresh goat's milk. Then you must eat your supper and go to bed. Go and sleep soundly."

During the night the wind howled and roared, and made the little hut tremble. The old man arose, saying to himself, "The child will be afraid." He went to Heidi's bedside. There she lay fast asleep. She must have been dreaming pleasant dreams, for happiness was on her little face.

When Heidi opened her eyes the next morning, the sun was shining through in the little round window of her room. She dressed quickly and went out in front of the hut. There was Peter, with his flock of goats, ready to go up the mountain.

"Would you like to go to the pasture with Peter and the goats?" asked her grandfather.

The child danced with delight. "Then eat your breakfast and be ready. You must be clean, or the sun will laugh at you," said the old man, as he went to prepare the lunch.

The two children went merrily up the mountain. During the night the wind had blown the last clouds away. The sky was deep

PETER AND HEIDI

blue, and in the centre stood the bright sun, sparkling upon the green Alps. Heidi ran hither and thither and shouted with joy. The mountain path led through great patches of fine, red primroses. Yonder it glistened all blue with the beautiful gentians, and everywhere laughed and nodded the tender-leaves, yellow rock-roses. In her delight over the glittering, nodding blossoms, Heidi even forgot the goats and Peter. Now here and now yonder shone the red and yellow, and drew the child in every direction.

So Peter had to look on all sides, and his round eyes, that did not move quickly from one thing to another, had more work than they could well manage. The goats also ran here and there, and the boy whistled and called and swung his staff to drive all the runaways together.

"Where are you, Heidi?" he called.

"Here," answered the child, not stirring from her seat among the blossoms.

"Come here," shouted Peter. "We have still a long way to climb. We must go on."

Higher and higher they climbed, until they came to the green grass where the goats usually pastured for the day. Peter threw himself on the ground to rest. The goats pushed their way into the bushes to find the sweet herbs.

Heidi sat down on the grass and looked about her. Far below lay the valley in the bright morning sunshine. In front a great, wide field of snow rose up toward the deep blue heavens, and a high tower of rocks seemed to look sternly down upon her.

For a long time she sat gazing at the rocks— so long that the lofty crags seemed to have faces and to be looking down at her like old friends. She heard the great eagle screaming in the air, and saw him flying in wide circles to his nest.

Suddenly, at Peter's whistle, the goats came jumping down the mountain. Heidi sprang up and ran toward them. She saw that the grandfather's goats, Little Swan and Little Bear, as they were called, were the finest in the flock.

"Of course they are," Peter said, "for the grandfather feeds them salt and washes them and has the best shed to keep them in." Peter knew each goat by name and could tell all its curious ways, perhaps because he had so little else to remember.

The white goat was milked for the noonday meal, and the children set out their bread and cheese upon the grass. Away bounded the goats again, climbing the rocky heights. After lunch, Heidi wandered about, picking the beautiful mountain blossoms.

And so the day passed, until the sun was beginning to sink down behind the mountains. Suddenly all the grass became golden, and the rocks above began to flash with rosy lights.

"Oh, look, Peter," shouted the child. "All the mountains are burning! Look at the rocks! See the beautiful snow! Everything is on fire."

"It is always so," answered Peter, good-naturedly; "but it is not fire."

"What is it then?" cried Heidi, as she sprang here and there, for she could not see enough, it was so beautiful on all sides. "Oh, look!" she cried out again. "See the lovely rosy snow! and on the rocks above are ever so many roses. Now they are turning gray; now they are gone."

"It will be just the same to-morrow," said Peter. "Come, we must go home now."

Peter whistled and called the goats together, and they started down the mountain. Heidi was silent, until she reached the hut and saw her grandfather sitting under the fir tree.

"Oh, Grandfather, the mountains are beautiful," she called out. "I saw the fire and the roses on the cliffs, and the blue and yellow flowers." Then she asked about the fire which she had seen at sunset.

"It is the sunshine," the grandfather explained. "When the sun says good-night to the mountains, he throws his most beautiful beams across them, so that they may not forget that he is coming back in the morning."

This pleased the little girl, and she could hardly wait for the morrow to come, so that she could go to the pasture again and see the sun bid good-night to the mountains. But first she must go to sleep; and she slept soundly the whole night long on her bed of hay, dreaming of bright, shining mountains, in the midst of which the goats merrily ran and jumped.

—Johanna Spyri.

Thinking about the Story

In a geography find a map of Europe; and on the map find the little country of Switzerland. Find pictures of the Alps, so that you may know the kind of country in which Heidi lived. Turn to the part of the geography that tells about Canada, and find pictures of Canadian mountains that look something like the Alps.

From the story, write down sentences that describe the Alps. Find sentences that tell what Grandfather thought of Heidi. Find other sentences that describe Heidi.

3. POPOCATEPETL

Another name for this mountain is "Smoking Mountain," but that name is not nearly so interesting as Popocatepetl, is it? You should practise saying it before you try to read the poem: Po-po-ca-te-petl.

My child, should you decide to go
And make your home in Mexico,
The proper place for you to settle
Is on Mount Popocatepetl.

Its slopes are green, its crest is white,
It's 18,000 feet in height;
The air will keep you in good fettle
On top of Popocatepetl.

Tall tropic trees grow here and there,
With flaming orchids, rich and rare;
No common weed or stinging nettle
Is found on Popocatepetl.

And if, on Summer days, your mind
Should turn to picnics, you'd not find
An easier place to boil a kettle
Than on Mount Popocatepetl.

But since the truth had best be told,
It suits the young—but not the old,

At eighty it may try your mettle
To climb Mount Popocatepetl.

—Hugh Chesterman.

Words and Volcanoes

One class, after reading "Popocatepetl," became interested in words and looked for other words as strange as "Popocatepetl." They used a geography to help them.

Another class became interested in volcanoes. They read about them, drew them, and modelled them.

---

4. A MARKET IN JAMAICA

This is a story about coloured children who work and play in Jamaica, an island in the Atlantic ocean far to the south of our country. It is much warmer there than here.

Hark to the cry of Naomi, the fruit-seller, in the market-place of Kingston, Jamaica: "Ripe bananas gwine pass! Buy yo' yams! Buy yo' sweet potatoes! Buy yo' pretty posies!" By her side are Virginia and Martha, her two daughters, girls of nine and ten. They have just come in from their little farm up-country, where Naomi's husband raises fruit and flowers.

All three have heavy baskets on their heads. These they do not hold up with their hands— they would scorn to do this. With head erect, chest flung forward, arms swinging freely,

mother and daughters have trudged cheerfully
and easily, with their head-loads, along the dusty
highways. Their cotton frocks are bright and
stiffly starched. Their teeth are white and
flashing. A gay handkerchief is knotted round
Naomi's head. When at length they lay their
baskets on the ground, it is hard to tell which
is the brighter—the colours in Naomi's turban,
or the colours of their flowers.

Many Negroes are there with their wares.
Some are people from the mountains to the

north of the city. These may have come by
train, for there is a good railway on the island,
or they may have brought their goods to market
on a donkey with baskets on each side.   In the
baskets are live fowls, eggs, or fruit. The father
rides the donkey. His wife walks. She has a
baby in her arms, and a basket of rare orchids
on her head. When the market is over, she will
put the pickaninny in one of the empty baskets,
and he will ride home.

One can buy all kinds of things in Kingston
market—pepper-pods and spices, baskets made
of coloured grass and snow-white reeds, walking-
sticks of ebony, or palm, or cinnamon wood;
jackass-rope, which is a name in Jamaica for
cheap tobacco.   It is sold by the yard!

In the middle of the court-yard is a fountain,
round which the tired donkeys rest with drooping head, or munch hot bundles of hay.   Here,
too, the merry children frisk about, heedless of
the sun.

When their flowers are sold, Virginia and
Martha join the other children at the fountain,
or perhaps they wander off to one of the piers,
to watch the famous diving boys.   These boys
are as much at home in the water as on land.

When the big ocean "liners" anchor in Kingston Bay, out shoot the diving boys in their small boats. They hope that some passenger will toss a ten-cent piece or a quarter overboard. When this happens, half a dozen boys plunge head-foremost into the sea. "Finders are keepers" is their motto, and soon one of them comes up with the prize. Then someone else tosses over a coin, and down they go once more!

The two girls think watching the diving boys is great fun. But they must not linger, for now the market will be over. They hasten back, and find their mother tying up the baskets. A cool breeze is blowing from the sea. The air is fresh and filled with the scent of wild flowers. Behind the mountains the sun is setting, as Naomi and her children walk peacefully back to their farm in beautiful Jamaica.

—*Adapted from* MARIE BAYNE.

MAKING A SCRAP-BOOK

Ask your teacher to divide the class into four groups to make a class scrap-book of pictures about hot countries. The book should have four parts: one part about the people who live in hot countries, another about the dwellings in which they live, another about the plants that grow there, another about the animals. Each group of pupils should find pictures for one of the four parts.

5. LATITUDE AND LONGITUDE

I often wonder when I see
A map—no matter which it be—
If all those lines that cross each page,
Like bars around a song-bird's cage,
Are merely signs to help my eye
And show me where the countries lie,
Or are they really, *really* there,
And do folk ever travel where
They lie so black?
What fun if some gigantic tram
Set from Hull or Amsterdam
Along the track.
The Tramcar man would say to me:
"This way, miss, for the Arctic Sea,
A penny, there and back."

—Hugh Chesterman.

6. A LETTER FROM INDIA

In this story a father, who has travelled to India, writes a letter to his children, Tom and Kate, in Canada. India is a part of the British Empire. Do you know where it is?

My dear Children,

Hurrah! I'm on shore again, after long, long days at sea. Yesterday, I reached Bombay, the chief seaport of India.

Soon after I landed, a friend whom I hadn't seen for many years came to call on me, and he took me for a drive around the city. I wish you had been with me to see the sights.

The streets are always thronged with people, and I think you would smile if you were to see how they are dressed. Most of them are barefoot, and very few of them have sleeves in their coats or frocks. The men usually wear white, and have turbans and sashes of yellow, green, or blue. The women wear a funny all-over garment that covers them from the neck to the knees, and they have many, very many, rings on their fingers and bracelets on their ankles and wrists. Some women even have rings in their noses and on their toes.

You would be amused to see the people carry-

ing great heavy burdens on their heads. Yesterday, as I came from the ship, I saw twelve men
carrying a grand piano on their heads. I watched
them as long as I could see them, and not
once did the piano teeter or shake as if it would
fall. People in India are taught to carry things
on their heads from the time they are very
small children, and as a result they hold themselves very straight.

Bombay is a very busy city. The streets are
thronged with carriages, automobiles, ox-carts,
and street-cars. As the people walk in the
middle of the road, it is not easy for carriages
to make their way through the streets. Yesterday

I heard a driver shout at a woman who had paid no attention to his warning bell. He said, "Hi, you woman with a baby on your hip, get out of the way!" A few minutes later he clanged his bell at a man and yelled at the top of his voice, "Hi, you man with a box on your head, get out of the way!"

I think you would like to see the ox-carts, and I have no doubt that Tom, at least, would want to ride in one. They are very small and are drawn by two oxen with humps on their shoulders. The driver sits on the shaft and steers the oxen with a stick.

To-morrow I am going out to visit the shops of Bombay, and my next letter to you will be about them. After that I am going up into the hills of India to visit your uncle and your cousin Hugh, who, as you know, is just the same age as Kate.

Best love,
Father.

—Agnes Fisher.

Writing a Letter

It is not likely that Hugh was ever in Canada. Write him a letter, telling him of all the things about a Canadian city or a Canadian farm that you think would be strange to him.

7. PARLIAMENT HILL

Have you seen the lights of London how they
    twinkle, twinkle, twinkle,
Yellow lights, and silver lights, and crimson
    lights, and blue?
And there among the other lights is Daddy's
    little lantern-light,
Bending like a finger-tip, and beckoning to you.

Never was so tall a hill for tiny feet to scramble
    up,
Never was so strange a world to baffle little eyes,
Half of it as black as ink with ghostly feet to
    fall on it,
And half of it all filled with lamps and cheerful
    sounds and cries.

Lamps in golden palaces, and station-lamps,
    and steamer-lamps,
Very nearly all the lamps that Mother ever knew,
And there among the other lamps is Daddy's
    little lantern lamp
Bending like a finger-tip, and beckoning to you.

—H. H. Bashford.

8. IN THE FAR NORTH

In the northern part of our own country are people of whom we hear very little.   Their way of living is so different from ours that you will find many surprises in this story.

Sitsak, the Eskimo, greets us at the door of his toupig. He lives away in the Far North. His forefathers dwelt on the shores of the Arctic Ocean long before the white man came to America.

The word "toupig" means tent. It is Sitsak's summer home, and is placed on the sea-shore. The tent is made of seal-skins sewn together by Sitsak's wife. This skin covering is spread over a framework of poles made from driftwood picked up on the shore. The framework is higher at the front than at the back.

Near the tent, Sitsak's kayak, or boat, is drawn up. It is also made of seal-skin over a framework of wood and whale-bone. In the middle is a hole in which Sitsak sits, and he uses a paddle broad at each end. The kayak is so light that Sitsak can carry it in one hand, yet seated in it he can brave the Arctic seas.

LAUNCHING THE KAYAK

There are other toupigs close by, for we have
come to a village; and since it is the time for
summer fishing, everyone is very busy. In the
late evening the men go out in their kayaks
to spread the nets, and soon they have to go
out again to bring in the catch.

In the Far North the sea teems with fish.
When the nets are brought in, there seems to be
a fish in every opening of the mesh, and three
or four men may catch a thousand in one
night.

The women are just as busy as the men.
Their task is to clean the fish and hang
them to dry in the sun. The dried fish are
then stored for the winter. They must be
well covered up, lest a hungry fox, or even a
polar bear should come along and help himself.

Summer is a merry time for the Eskimo
children. The sun shines till midnight, so
they cannot go to sleep. Their mothers do
not even say, "Time to go to bed!" They
may stay up as long as they please, or as
long as they can keep their eyes open.

In summer there are many other children
to play with, for this is the time of year

when the Eskimo visits his friends. The shore-waters being no longer ice-bound, he comes with his wife and children in long, skin boats called "u-miaks." These have many rowers.

Friend or stranger is made welcome in the Eskimo's tent. When the day's work is over, they share their fish supper, and then they chat or tell stories by the light of the midnight sun.

Only in the short summer, however, can Sitsak live in a toupig. When the dark days come, and the great freeze-up sets in, he must build a nice warm hut. The frame of this hut may be of driftwood, or of stones, or even of blocks of snow, but it is always covered with sods. The roof is kept up by poles.

A stove is used for cooking, but the house is heated by a number of lamps, which burn all night long. Sitsak's wife trims them carefully to prevent them from smoking.

There is only one room in the Eskimo house. Round the wall runs a low bench or platform, on which the family eat and sleep. The bed-clothes are soft bear skins.

In the autumn Sitsak goes off in his dog-sledge to hunt. He hunts the caribou, the flesh of which he counts a great treat. Of caribou hide he can make very many things—harness for the dogs, clothes, boots, and gloves.

Sitsak's dress is of caribou skin. In winter he wears two coats. His under-coat has the fur next his body, while his upper coat has the fur outside. Both coats have hoods and lappets for his ears, for he must not get frost-bite.

Sitsak's wife and his children are dressed almost in the same way as himself. His wife carries the baby in her hood, where it is very cosy. An Eskimo's clothes have no hooks and eyes, or buttons and button-holes—but just drawing strings and a leather belt. If an Eskimo feels cold, he tightens his belt, and if he feels warm, he loosens it.

In deep mid-winter the sun is not seen at all, and there are only a few hours of day-light. This light is dim and cold, but all night long the stars shine very brightly.

At this time of year, Sitsak may build an "igloo" or snow-house, which is warmer still. It looks like a great white bowl turned up-

side down.   The windows are blocks of ice,
and in the roof is a hole instead of a stove-pipe.

Many Eskimos live far away where they
have never seen a white man.   But those who
live on the mainland of Canada are often visited
by explorers and trappers, and have learned
more of the ways of the white man.

—Marie Bayne.

Finding Ways to Make Things

To make an igloo, save the paraffin tops from your
mother's jelly jars.   Melt the paraffin, and pour it, a
spoonful at a time, over a small bowl until the bowl has a
thick coat of paraffin.   Take out the bowl, and there is
your igloo, except for the door and the smoke-hole.   How
would you make the other two kinds of Eskimo lodges?

How would you make a model of a kayak?

In a model Eskimo village, how would you show the sea?

---

9. LITTLE MAID OF FAR JAPAN

Little maid upon my fan,
Did you come from far Japan?
What a tiny oval face!
Do you like this other place?

Do you miss the cherry trees
Where you knew the little breeze,

Where you heard the cuckoo sing
In the spring?

Then you crossed your lattice floor,
Flung aside your paper door,
Joined the other maids at play,
Far away.

Now you live upon my fan,
Little maid of far Japan,
Still, you have a merry face—
Do you like this other place?

—ANNETTE WYNNE.

FINDING FACTS

In many ways, children in eastern countries live differently from the way you live. From books in the library, find five ways in which their customs are different.

It may help you with your work if you think of the eastern children's food, houses, dress; the way in which they keep warm; the work they do; how they play.

HIGHDAYS & HOLIDAYS

1. A GOOD THANKSGIVING

On Thanksgiving Day everyone can give something away, even if just a happy smile. Read the poem to see what happens when people begin giving things away.

Said Old Gentleman Gay: "On a Thanksgiving
   Day,
If you want a good time, then give something
   away."
So he sent a fat turkey to Shoemaker Price,
And the shoemaker said: "What a big bird!
   how nice!
And since a good dinner's before me, I ought
To give old Widow Lee the small chicken I
   bought."

"This fine chicken, oh, see!" said the pleased
   Widow Lee,

"And the kindness that sent it, how precious
to me!
I should like to make someone as happy as
I—
I'll give Washwoman Biddy my big pumpkin
pie."

"And, oh, sure," Biddy said, " 'tis the queen
of all pies!
Just to look at its yellow face gladdens my
eyes.
Now it's my turn, I think; and a sweet ginger
cake
For the motherless Finigan children I'll
bake."

"A cake, all our own! T'is too good to be
true!"
Said the Finigan children, Rose, Denny, and
Hugh.
"It smells sweet of spice, and we'll carry a
slice
To little lame Jake—who has nothing that's
nice."

"Oh, I thank you, and thank you !" said little
lame Jake.

"Oh, what beautiful, beautiful, beautiful cake!
And such a big slice! I will save all the
    crumbs,
And will give them to each little sparrow that
    comes!"
And the sparrows they twittered as if they
    would say,
Like Old Gentleman Gay: "On a Thanksgiv-
    ing Day,
If you want a good time, then give something
    away."
                                —MARIAN DOUGLAS.

A KINDNESS CHAIN

This poem is like a chain of kindness. Draw a chain with large links, and in each link write the name of the person who was kind, the kindness he did, and the name of the person to whom he was kind.

2. THE JACK-O'-LANTERN

On Hallowe'en we like to make jack-o'-lanterns and
to carry about their funny, grinning faces. But long ago
a boy made a jack-o'-lantern that saved the lives of his
mother and his little brothers and sisters. Would a
jack-o'-lantern frighten anyone who did not know what
it was?

Sam was a boy who lived in a log cabin in
great woods that were full of Indians. His
father was making a little farm in the woods,
and every year he cut down trees to make room
for potatoes and corn. Between the corn rows
he planted pumpkins. Sam went to school
when he could, but often he had to help his
father with the work of the farm.

When Sam was ten years old, his father
one day had to go to town to buy salt
and other things that he could not grow
on the farm. It was fifteen miles to the
nearest town, and though he went on horse-
back, he could not get back before evening.

He told Sam to take good care of his
mother and the little children. If they saw
Indians in the woods, they must all run
into the house and shut the door. The
Indians were afraid of Sam's father with

his gun, but if they knew that he was away, and that there was no one to protect the family, they might come and kill them.

All morning long Sam worked hard. He husked the corn and brought home pumpkins from the field and stored them. But all the time he kept watching the woods for Indians.

In the afternoon he suddenly remembered that it was Hallowe'en, and asked his mother whether he might make a jack-o'-lantern.

"Have you chopped all the wood?" she asked.

"Yes, Mother."

"Have you filled the water pails?"

"Yes, Mother."

"Have you dug the potatoes for supper?"

"Yes, Mother."

"Then you may make a jack-o'-lantern."

So Sam found a good, round pumpkin. First he dug out the inside, and then he carefully cut holes for the eyes and a great wide slit for a mouth. He made two rows of teeth that looked as if they could chew up anything. All the children watched Sam as he made his jack-o'-lantern.

When it was finished, he put a candle

in it and told the children that he would light it when night came.

"I do wish your father would come," said Sam's mother, as she sat rocking the baby. "He is very late. When he is away, I am always afraid of the Indians."

She put the baby to bed and prepared the supper. Sam's father did not come. At last they all ate their supper. Still the father did not come.

The children begged that the jack-o'-lantern might be lighted before they went to bed, so Sam and his mother carried the pumpkin to the window and set it on the sill. Then Sam lighted a splinter of wood at the fire and went to light the candle.

If he had looked out of the window, what do you think he would have seen? He would have seen shadows moving near the house. He would have seen Indians stealing from tree to tree, just as you do when you play hide-and-seek. They were coming nearer and nearer. They had found out that the man with the gun was not at home.

But Sam was lighting the candle in the jack-o'-lantern.

"Who-o-o-op!" came a great yell outside.

"Indians," whispered Sam's mother.

Sam peeked out into the darkness and saw the Indians running away as fast as they could. It was no wonder they ran, for never had they seen such a creature. Two eyes of fire blazed at them, and a great red mouth full of terrible teeth grinned at them out of the darkness. They must have thought it was some strange goblin.

Soon afterwards, Sam's father came home, leading his horse. It had fallen lame, and he had had to walk the last part of the way.

"Well, well," he said, when he heard what

had happened. "That's a new use for a jack-o'-lantern."

—Author Unknown.

Hallowe'en Sentences

Here are some sentences that play Hallowe'en tricks. The sentences are jumbled. Can you straighten them out?

1. Lived Sam days the early in.
2. Made Sam Hallowe'en on jack-o'-lantern a.
3. Days those in woods the were Indians of full.
4. Night Hallowe'en came house Sam's to they on.
5. Window Sam jack-o'-lantern put the in the.
6. Away scared jack-o'-lantern them the.
7. Jack-o'-lantern father it Sam's said was use new a for a.

---

3. THE MAGIC VINE

A Fairy seed I planted,
  So dry and white and old;
There sprang a vine enchanted,
  With magic flowers of gold.

I watched it, I tended it,
  And truly, by and by,
It bore a Jack-O'-Lantern,
  And a big Thanksgiving pie.

—Author Unknown.

4. "THERE WERE SHEPHERDS"

We must never forget that Christmas Day is the birthday of our Lord. Our gifts to one another and all our happiness should remind us of God's great gift to us when on that day, long ago, Christ was born. This is part of the story of the first Christmas, as told by one who lived then.

There were in the same country shepherds abiding in the field, keeping watch over their flock by night.

And, lo, the angel of the Lord came upon them, and the glory of the Lord shone round about them: and they were sore afraid.

And the angel said unto them, "Fear not; for, behold, I bring you good tidings of great joy, which shall be to all people.

"For unto you is born this day, in the city of David, a Saviour, which is Christ the Lord.

"And this shall be a sign unto you; Ye shall find the babe wrapped in swaddling clothes, lying in a manger."

And suddenly there was with the angel a multitude of the heavenly host praising God, and saying,

"THERE WERE SHEPHERDS"

"Glory to God in the highest, and on earth peace, good will toward men."

And it came to pass, as the angels were gone away from them into heaven, the shepherds said one to another, "Let us now go even unto Bethlehem, and see this thing which is come to pass, which the Lord hath made known unto us."

And they came with haste, and found Mary, and Joseph, and the babe lying in a manger.

—THE BIBLE.

REMEMBERING

Learn the angel's speech and the chorus of the heavenly host so that you can think them correctly without looking at the book. Start with "And the angel said unto them . . ." and learn the words down to "good will toward men."

And when the wise men from the east were come into the house, they saw the young child with Mary His mother, and fell down and worshipped Him: and when they had opened their treasures, they presented unto Him gifts; gold, and frankincense, and myrrh.

—ST. MATTHEW II: 11.

5. A CHILD'S SONG OF CHRISTMAS

This poem is *really* a child's song of Christmas, for it
was written by the poet when she was a little girl in Toronto.
As you read the poem, you will see that she is thinking of
two Christmases.   What are they?

My counterpane is soft as silk,
My blankets white as creamy milk;
The hay was soft to Him, I know,
Our little Lord of long ago.

Above the roof the pigeons fly
In silver wheels across the sky;
The stable-doves they cooed to them,
Mary and Christ in Bethlehem.

Bright shines the sun across the drifts,
And bright upon my Christmas gifts;
They brought Him incense, myrrh, and gold,
Our little Lord who lived of old.

Oh, soft and clear our mother sings
Of Christmas joys and Christmas things;
God's holy angels sang to them,
Mary and Christ in Bethlehem.

Our hearts they hold all Christmas dear,
And earth seems sweet, and heaven seems near;

Oh, heaven was in His sight, I know,
That little Child of long ago.

—MARJORIE L. C. PICKTHALL.

READING A TWO-PART POEM

This poem has a beautiful sound when a class reads it aloud together. The best way to read it is to choose a good reader to read the first two lines of each verse. The whole class should read the second two lines.

"A Child's Song of Christmas" is two poems in one. Find the two poems, and write them out separately.

---

6. WHY?

Why do bells for Christmas ring?
Why do little children sing?
Once a lovely shining star,
Seen by shepherds from afar,
Gently moved until its light
Made a manger cradle bright.

There a darling Baby lay,
Pillowed soft upon the hay;
And Its mother sang and smiled,
"This is Christ, the Holy Child,"
Therefore bells for Christmas ring,
Therefore, little children sing!

—LYDIA A. COONLEY WARD.

7. A VISIT FROM ST. NICHOLAS

Dr. Moore made up this poem on his way home from buying a Christmas turkey for a poor family. He recited the poem to his children as a surprise, and they liked it so well that they learned it all by heart.

'Twas the night before Christmas, when all
    through the house
Not a creature was stirring, not even a mouse;
The stockings were hung by the chimney with
    care,
In hopes that St. Nicholas soon would be there;
The children were nestled all snug in their beds,
While visions of sugar-plums danced in their
    heads;
And mamma in her kerchief, and I in my cap,
Had just settled our brains for a long winter's
    nap,—
When out on the lawn there arose such a clatter,
I sprang from my bed to see what was the
    matter.

Away to the window I flew like a flash,
Tore open the shutters, and threw up the sash.
The moon on the breast of the new-fallen snow
Gave a lustre of mid-day to objects below,

ST. NICHOLAS

When what to my wondering eyes should appear
But a miniature sleigh, and eight tiny reindeer.
With a little old driver, so lively and quick,
I knew in a moment it must be St. Nick.

More rapid than eagles his coursers they came,
And he whistled and shouted, and called them
    by name:
"Now, Dasher! now, Dancer! now, Prancer and
    Vixen!
On, Comet! on, Cupid! on, Donder and Blitzen!
To the top of the porch! to the top of the wall!
Now dash away! dash away! dash away, all!"
As dry leaves that before the wild hurricane fly,
When they meet with an obstacle, mount to the
    sky,
So up to the housetop the coursers they flew
With the sleigh full of toys,—and St. Nicholas,
    too.

And then in a twinkling I heard on the roof
The prancing and pawing of each little hoof;
As I drew in my head, and was turning around,
Down the chimney St. Nicholas came with a
    bound.
He was dressed all in fur from his head to his
    foot,

And his clothes were all tarnished with ashes
    and soot;
A bundle of toys he had flung on his back,
And he looked like a pedlar just opening his
    pack.
His eyes—how they twinkled! his dimples—how
    merry!
His cheeks were like roses, his nose like a
    cherry!

His droll little mouth was drawn up like a bow,
And the beard on his chin was as white as the
    snow;
The stump of a pipe he held tight in his teeth,
And the smoke it encircled his head like a
    wreath.
He had a broad face, and a little round belly
That shook when he laughed like a bowl full
    of jelly.
He was chubby and plump,—a right jolly old
    elf,—
And I laughed, when I saw him, in spite of
    myself.

A wink of his eye and a twist of his head
Soon gave me to know I had nothing to dread.

He spoke not a word, but went straight to his
 work
And filled all the stockings; then turned with
 a jerk,
And laying his finger aside of his nose,
And giving a nod, up the chimney he rose.
He sprang to his sleigh, to his team gave a
 whistle,
And away they all flew like the down of a
 thistle.
But I heard him exclaim, ere he drew out of
 sight,
"Happy Christmas to all! and to all a good-
 night!"

—CLEMENT C. MOORE.

THINKING ABOUT THE POEM

1. Who is speaking in this poem?
2. What were the children doing?
3. What were the names of the reindeer?
4. Why was St. Nicholas in such haste?
5. What made his clothes "tarnished with ashes and
soot?"
6. Why were his eyes twinkling?
7. "I laughed in spite of myself." Why?
8. Why did he not speak a word?
9. "Away they all flew." Where did they go?
10. Find all the words and phrases that show St. Nicholas
to be a "merry old soul."

8. NEW YEAR'S DAYS

The New Year begins when the snow and ice are here for merry games outdoors. Even the wind seems to whistle a song for the glad New Year.

The New Year's days are white with snow,
The winds are laughing as they blow.
Across the ponds and lakes we glide,
And o'er the drifting snow we ride,
And down the hills we gaily slide,
    For it is winter weather.

Each rushing stream is warmly dress'd,
An icy coat upon its breast,
And on each branch of every tree,

261

Packed in as close as close can be,
The next year's leaflets we can see,
All nestled close together.

—CELIA STANDISH.

A HOLIDAY CALENDAR

For each of the holidays in the year, draw a picture that will make people think of that day. Below each picture print the calendar for the month in which the holiday comes.

————————

9. MAH SING'S VALENTINE

Valentine was a priest who lived long ago in the city of Rome. He taught the boys in the monastery school to love flowers. Whenever a boy was ill, Valentine would send him some flowers and a kindly message. This became a custom that has spread all over the world. Long after Valentine's death he was given the name of St. Valentine, and the fourteenth of February is St. Valentine's Day.

Everyone was happy at the little school at Welcome Landing after the new teacher had come, for she was very kind and made the work in school interesting. Mah Sing, the Chinese boy, thought her very nice indeed, and did all he could to please her.

It was the thirteenth day of February, and the teacher was helping the children to make

valentines for the next day.   Now Mah Sing
was puzzled about this St. Valentine's Day.
So he asked his friend, Billy, to explain it to
him.   "Is it like Christmas?" he asked.

"Oh, no," answered Billy, who was in the
eighth grade. "At Christmas we give presents
to a lot of people.   But on St. Valentine's
Day you just send a card or a present to
somebody special, and you don't tell who
sent it.   The present may be flowers, or
something to eat, like candy."

"What is on the card?" asked Mah Sing.

"Oh, some sort of picture, like a heart with
an arrow in it, or a cupid with an arrow; and
a verse like this:

'The rose is red, the violet's blue;
Sugar is sweet, and so are you.'"

Mah Sing thought deeply as he went along
the rocky trail to his home.   There were no
flowers at Welcome Landing in February, and
it would be almost as hard to find candy
as flowers.   He would so love to send a
valentine to dear Teacher — but what was he
to give her?   And how could he ever make a

card with a picture and a poem on it?

Billy had said the gift might be something to eat, and the only thing to eat that Mah Sing could get would be a fish. So, when he reached home, he asked leave to go out fishing in the row-boat.

Through the channels between the islands he rowed on until he felt a tug at his line, and quickly reeled in. But he found that a dog-fish had taken his bait. This is a small kind of shark, which kills the other fish.

The winter afternoon was drawing to a close, and Mah Sing knew that he must soon go home. So he got rid of the dog-fish and went on rowing. Jerk! Another fish was on his line — not a shark this time, he hoped. No; it was a good-sized rock-cod. It was not pretty to look at, but good in the frying-pan.

He rowed back to the wharf, and made the cod look as nice as he could, placing it in a flat basket.

So far, good; but the hardest task was still to come—the card with a picture and a poem. He had no idea what a cupid looked like, so he thought he would make a drawing of himself in the boat.

He spent a happy half-hour over his picture, and then trouble came again. What was the poem Billie had told him? "Rosie red, something is blue; you are sweet, like sugar," he murmured, and shook his head.

That was not poetry. Also it was not true. Teacher was not red and blue, neither was she good to eat like sugar. Teacher made him think of beautiful things.

Mah Sing went to the door and stood gazing out over the harbour at the sunset. Then he sat down and wrote,

"The sky is gray, and across it there are lines of yellow. The fir trees near my home are green, and you, also, are like that, dear Teacher."

Teacher smiled when she read the valentine. "Dear little Mah Sing!" she said.

—*Adapted from* HELEN DICKSON.

THINKING ABOUT THE STORY

Read through the story, and find a sentence that tells each of the following things:

1. That the teacher liked Mah Sing.
2. That the children wanted a Valentine party.
3. That Welcome Landing was a small place.
4. That Mah Sing liked pretty things.
5. That Mah Sing was poor.
6. That Mah Sing did not live in a cold climate. (Welcome Landing is in Canada; where could it be?)

---

10. THE FIRST EASTER BUNNY

Characters:

SPRING, BUNNY, BIG BEAR, ROBIN, FOX, SQUIRREL, and other ANIMALS.

SCENE: *A clearing in a wood; a mossy bank on one side.*

SPRING (*running in, laughing, and scattering flowers*). Oh, it is good to be back! My own dear woods! I thought I should never see you

again. Every time I tried to come, the North
Wind drove me away. But yesterday I heard a
child crying, and I think I heard her calling me;
so of course I had to come. No one could stay
away when a child was crying! Then when I
really came, the North Wind turned and ran.
It was too funny. To think that all I had to
do was just to stop being afraid, and come anyway. But how lonely the woods look! Where
is everyone? (*Puts a little flute to her lips and
blows a long clear note; a robin answers, and a
rabbit hops out.*)

BUNNY. Dear Lady Spring, we thought you
had forgotten us!

SPRING. Oh, Bunny, I am so glad to see you!
I have had a dreadful time, thinking I could not
get here just because that old North Wind blew
so loud. Where is everyone?

BUNNY. Where's everyone in winter time?
They came trooping out to meet you, and then,
when you did not come, they all trooped back
again. It was so lonely without you. Big
Bear vowed he'd sleep the whole year round
unless you came. Two robins arrived on time,
but they have been in a terrible flutter for fear
they could never build a nest or raise a family.

The squirrel's cupboard is empty, and old Grandfather Squirrel is lean as a bone.

SPRING. I am so sorry, Bunny!

BUNNY. Even the children have gone. One child watched and waited for you every day. I heard her crying in the woods, because she thought you would not come in time for Easter.

SPRING (*softly*). Ah, that was what brought me back. There is no wind so loud that it can drown the crying of a child. Oh, Bunny, I'm *so* glad I came! (*Laughing.*) Now we must wake everyone. (*She runs to a log and knocks.*) Wake up, wake up, old sleepy head!

VOICE (*growling inside a log*). What's that? G-r-r-r, how warm it grows! I smell nice warm earth! G-r-r-r. I smell honey!

(*A thumping and bumping is heard from inside the log, and Big Bear comes out.*)

BIG BEAR. Spring! Bless my soul, Spring! Well, you've been long enough coming! G-r-r-r. I'm glad to see you. (*Goes to Spring and gives her a bear hug.*)

SPRING. Oh, Big Bear, don't hug so hard! You will scare me away again!

BIG BEAR (*growling frightfully*). Then don't wait so long next time if you want us to treat you more gently!   That hug has been growing ever since the time you should have been here!   (*Stretches his big paws.*)   My! I'm glad to be awake.   Hello, Bunny!   Where's everybody?

SPRING.   They must be still asleep.   I'll call them again.   (*Puts the flute to her lips and plays a little tune.*)

(*Out from the wood come creatures—a fox, a squirrel, other rabbits, etc.—and dance about Spring.   Spring dances in the centre of the ring faster and faster until she throws herself down on the moss.   The animals cluster about her.*)

SPRING.   Isn't it jolly to be back again?   Now we are all here but the children.   Where are the children?   We want the children.

ANIMALS.   Oh, yes! We want the children.

BUNNY.   Dear Lady Spring, I am afraid they will not come again.   Last time they hunted for you everywhere; and when they could not find you, they said good-bye to trees and brook and went away so sadly.   It was too cold and dreary in the woods for them.

SPRING.   Just see the mischief I have done by being afraid of that old North Wind!   We must have the children, though.   Oh, I know what to do.   One of you shall take a message to them so that they will know that I am here. Big Bear, will you go?

BIG BEAR. Me? Bless my soul, if they saw me coming, they would be so frightened that they would never wait to hear what I had to say.

SPRING. I am afraid that is so.   Robin, will you go?

ROBIN. I would go most gladly, but my wife is already beginning our nest, and I must help her every minute.   Send the fox.

FOX (*licking his lips*).   Oh, yes! I will go.

SPRING. Wait a minute.   The road to the village goes past Farmer Brown's hen-house. I fear my message would never reach the children.

FOX. Why would you think such a thing of me?

SPRING. That is what comes of having a bad reputation.   Squirrel, will you go?

SQUIRREL. Not I! Last time I went to the village a man tried to catch me.   No, I like the children, but my treetop is the safest place for me.

BUNNY I will go, Lady Spring!

SPRING. You are not afraid, Bunny?

BUNNY. Afraid? Not a bit of it! I will go at night when the men-folk are asleep, and if a dog sees me, I'll lead him a pretty chase into a brier-patch. It won't be the first time. But what will you send so that the children will understand?

SPRING. We will make some tiny baskets of the greenest moss that grows and fill them with the daintiest of spring flowers. That is a message every child can read.

FOX. How can you be sure that the baskets all go to children? What if a grown-up should find one first?

SPRING. He will not understand the message unless he has the heart of a child, and if he has that heart, then he belongs to us, and we to him. So the message cannot go astray. Now, all to work!

(*They run to the mossy bank; some shape baskets, some gather flowers.*)

ROBIN. Here is a wake-robin. They will all know that came from me.

SQUIRREL. Here are some acorns that have sprouted. There is no need to tell a child who sent those.

BIG BEAR. That is too dainty work for my

big paws. But still I think there's something needful I can do. (*Lumbers off and comes back with a birch-bark basket with a bark strap.*) There, hang that on Bunny's shoulders, and pack it carefully with messages.

SPRING. You dear old bear! It is exactly what we need. Now bring all the messages! And we shall call our messenger the Easter Bunny.

(*The animals bring moss baskets to Bunny, who packs them in the big basket.*)

BUNNY (*packing the basket*). Here's a marsh-marigold, yellow as wee Molly's hair— I know where to leave that. This one with innocents, blue as a baby's eyes, must be for Baby Gretchen. The wake-robin is for Sandy, who cared for the robin with the broken wing, and this with acorns for the boy who scattered nuts for the squirrels last winter. Here's a spring beauty for the child who cried for spring. Wise Lady Spring, how plain the message is for every child. Help me on with the basket; I must be off.

(*And away goes the Easter Bunny.*)

—FRANCES GILLESPY WICKES.

11. AN ARBOUR DAY TREE

Arbour Day means Tree Day, the day when the school children plant trees to beautify their school grounds.

Dear little tree that we plant to-day,
What will you be when we're old and gray?
"The savings bank of the squirrel and mouse,
For robin and wren an apartment house,
The dressing-room of the butterfly's ball,
The locust's and katydid's concert hall,
The school-boy's ladder in pleasant June,
The school-girl's tent in the July noon,

And my leaves shall whisper them merrily
A tale of the children who planted me."

—Author Unknown.

Arbour Day at School

In many parts of Canada, the children have no regular lessons on the first Friday in May. Instead, they clean out cupboards, rake the lawns, make flower beds, and in every way help to make the school and grounds bright and beautiful. Do you do that in your school?

---

12. BIRD-HOUSE DAY

Birds are cheerful neighbours and useful too. The children in this story had a good plan to make sure of having bird neighbours.

The five Jarvis children, Charlie, Sue, Tom, Fred, and Esther, were to help plant the new orchard. Their father gave each of them a tiny tree, and on Arbour Day morning, Jim, the hired man, went with them, to show them how to plant their trees properly.

It was a warm, sunny morning in May, and as they worked they could hear birds singing. There were birds in the boughs of the trees of the old orchard, and birds in the elms that lined the driveway.

Sue stopped work to listen to them. "I hope," she said, "that the birds will come to our orchard. I love to hear them sing."

"I like blue-birds best," said Charlie, "and I want blue-birds to make nests in my tree."

"They won't until it's old enough to have a hole in it," said Tom. "And then it must be the right kind of hole."

"What kind?"

"One with a little ledge outside, or else a little twig in front, so that they can alight before going in."

"You don't need to wait for your tree to be old, Charlie," Esther said; "you can put up a bird-house, which will do just as well."

"But even so, he'll have to wait till the tree is bigger," said Fred.

"How long?" asked Charlie.

"Well," said Jim, "it takes a long time for a tree to get started. But you needn't wait for that. Birds are good partners to have in this fruit-raising business. The more birds there are around, the fewer insects there will be to eat your trees, and the faster they will grow. Why don't you put some bird-houses in the old orchard and in the elms?"

"Will you help us?" asked Tom.

"Indeed I will," replied Jim. "But you must hurry, for there's no time to lose. The birds are coming every day."

"I want to put a tree-swallow house in the elm," said Fred. "Tree-swallows eat insects, too. They catch them on the wing."

"So do the purple martins," said Tom. "Let's make a martin house."

"And a wren house on the porch," said Esther.

"Blue-birds served first," said Jim. "All of you spend the afternoon hunting small boxes to make them of, and this evening we'll get them ready. On Saturday we'll put them up."

"And we'll call Saturday 'Bird-house Day!'" exclaimed Sue.

"Oh, yes!" cried Esther. "Let's tell the girls and boys at school. Almost all of them are going to plant something to-day, and they'll want to have birds around, too. We could have a 'Bird-house Day' every year, just as we have Arbour Day."

"We'll have a 'Bird-house Day' of our own, anyway," said Tom. "I think that's a great idea. Don't you, Jim?"

"First rate. Only next year you must begin earlier to get ready for it. We'll be making the boxes through the winter, and have our 'Bird-house Day' before the birds get here."

"My!" said Charlie, "won't the birds be surprised to find so many nice houses *to let*? How much rent shall we ask?"

"Oh!" said Jim, with a laugh, "any bird can have a nest 'for a song.' "

—Elizabeth Hill.

Studying Birds

How many different kinds of birds live near your home? You may be surprised at how many there are.

One of the most interesting things to do in the spring and early summer is to make a "bird count."

To make a "bird count," each pupil describes and names the birds that he saw the day before.

The keeper of the bird records writes the names of the birds, when, where, and by whom seen.

278 HIGHDAYS AND HOLIDAYS

13. ONLY ONE MOTHER

When you have read this verse that the poet has written
to his mother, write a verse of your own to *your* mother.
Think carefully what you wish to say to her.

Hundreds of stars in the pretty sky;
   Hundreds of shells on the shore together;
Hundreds of birds that go singing by;
   Hundreds of bees in the sunny weather.
Hundreds of dewdrops to greet the dawn;
   Hundreds of lambs in the purple clover;
Hundreds of butterflies on the lawn;
   But only one mother the wide world over.

—GEORGE COOPER.

MEMORIZING A POEM

Try memorizing the poem this way: Cut four strips of
paper, the first one half an inch wide, the next one an inch
wide, and so on. Now lay the narrowest strip on the middle
of the poem, and read it, trying to remember what is under
the strip. When you can do this without any mistakes,
use the inch strip, then the wider ones, until you can think
the poem when it is all covered.

Should fairies three all come to me,
   And say, "What gifts are best?"
I'm sure I'd say, "Bring gifts to-day
   Of love, and peace, and rest."

14. A PRINCESS BECOMES A QUEEN

Have you ever wondered why we have a holiday on the twenty-fourth of May? Read this story, and you will understand why we honour that day.

It was the early morning of June twentieth, in the year 1837. Everyone in Kensington Palace was sound asleep, for it was so early that not even the birds had wakened to sing the songs with which they greet the day.

Suddenly there came a knocking at the palace door; no one answered. Again and again the knocking was repeated, until at last a drowsy-eyed servant came in answer to it. Sleepy though he was, he knew at once the two men who waited at the door. One was the Archbishop of Canterbury, the other the Lord Chamberlain. But what could have brought them at such an early hour?

"We have come to see the Princess Victoria," said one of the visitors. The servant, now wide awake and very excited, at once hurried away to give the message to the princess's lady-in-waiting.

The two men waited impatiently. After what seemed to them a very long time, the

lady-in-waiting entered the room where they sat.

"My lords," she said, "can your errand not wait? The princess is in such a sweet sleep that I dare not waken her."

"Madam," said the Lord Chamberlain gravely, "this is no time for waiting. Pray tell the princess that we wish to see her on business of state."

In a few minutes the door opened softly, and the princess, wearing a dressing-gown and slippers, entered. The lady-in-waiting followed, throwing a shawl over the shoulders of the young princess, and smoothing her long, fair hair.

No sooner had the princess entered the room than the two men rose from their places, and kneeled before her. As he kissed her hand, the Archbishop said, "The King is dead; long live the Queen."

She was queen—ruler of a great empire. Her lands stretched far over the sea, and her people lived in every part of the globe. The thought of it all frightened her; tears filled her eyes, and for a few moments she could not speak. At last, in a low voice she said to the Archbishop, "I ask your prayers on my behalf."

So began the reign of good Queen Victoria. She was only a girl of eighteen at the time, and for over sixty years she was our queen. Every year we honour her memory by observing as a holiday Victoria Day—the twenty-fourth of May, the date on which she was born.

—Jessie E. McEwen.

15. CANADA'S CHILD

Are you Canada's child?

Do you wander her meadows, gather her bright
　　flowers,
Do you walk her gray streets, follow her winding
　　roads on your way to school?
Are you Canada's child?

Come, then, little Ellaf, with your pale shining
　　hair and sea-blue eyes.
You are Canada's child now.　You are from
　　Iceland; your fathers are known in the world.
They are strong and brave; they are fearless men.
They dared the wild waves a thousand years
　　ago.
Will you be strong and brave here in your new
　　home?

Come then, little Ileana, what have you brought
　　from your deep hidden valleys,
From your grandmother's whitewashed cottage
　　with the thatched roof?
Have you remembered her patterns?　Are they
　　woven into your mind?　Show us her tapes-
　　tries.

Show us her old embroideries, give us the bright
   threads into our clumsy hands;
Our cloth is plain and new; teach us your colours.

Come then, little Matsumoto, tell us of what
   you love.
Tell us of cherry blossoms, of waterfalls, of
   temples, of old mountains,
Read to us your poems, painted with hair-fine
   brushes on shining silk.
Our country is so big. Make us look at it
   closely, Matsumoto, make our eyes see in it
The small perfect things that give you joy.

Come then, Sonia, with your pointed chin and
   delicate hands;
What do you bring, from the old land that was
   yours? Do you bring music,
Do you bring dark songs in your heart, the songs
   of those who loved their country
And were driven away? Sing them to us; they
   are beautiful.

Come then, dark-eyed Yvonne. Why, we cannot
   say "come" to you!
You have been Canada's child for three hundred
   years.

You are here too, little Daphne, with your ash-
blond hair,
With your pink cheeks and your clear English
gaze; you are our older sister.
And you, Bruce, from the rugged northern glens,
You have been our strength from the beginning.

What can we say to you, Running Wolf,
little brother?
Will you tell us what the wind means when it
blows in the autumn?
Will you show us the ways of the forest?

You are all Canada's children now, you, Ileana,
you, Matsumoto, you, little Loyze;
You, Ellaf, you, Margarita, you, John, and
Michael.

You are all Canada's children now:
What do you bring to her in your small warm
hands?

—FRANCES SHELLEY WEES.

A PAGEANT FOR DOMINION DAY

Just after school closes comes Dominion Day. Some
classes have a "Canada Birthday Party" the last day of
school.

For the party, "Canada's Child" makes a very pretty
pageant. Ask your teacher what a pageant is, and if you
like the idea, she may let you have one.

16. VACATION TIME

Here we are at the end of the year and the end of the book! And is not this a suitable poem for the last day and the last page?

Good-bye, little desk at school, good-bye,
We're off to the fields and the open sky.
The bells of the brooks and the woodland bells
Are ringing us out to the vales and dells,
To meadow-ways fair, and to hilltops cool,
Good-bye, little desk at school.

Good-bye, little desk at school, good-bye,
We've other brave lessons and tasks to try;
But we shall come back in the fall, you know,
And as gay to come as we are to go,
With ever a laugh and never a sigh—
Good-bye, little desk, good-bye!

—FRANK HUTT.

A LITTLE DICTIONARY

ă as in fat   ĕ as in met   ĭ as in bit   ŏ as in hot   ŭ as in but
ā as in fate   ē as in me   ī as in bite   ō as in hole   ū as in pure
à as in class   ê as in herd   y as in story   ộ as in awe
ä as in alms   ōō as in foot   ow as in how
å as in fare   o͞o as in room   oy as in boy

th as in think   th as in that   zh as in azure

An unmarked vowel is a slightly shortened vowel, usually unaccented.

ancient (ān′shent): old, long ago.
applauded (a-plôd′ed): cheered.

banian (băn′yan): an Indian tree which sends out large branches that droop to the ground and take root.
bravo (brä′vō): well done!
brilliant (brĭl′yant): very bright.
buffet (bŭ-fā′): sideboard.
bulrushes (bōōl′rŭsh-ez): large plants that grow in wet places.
burglars (bêrg′lẽrz): those who break into houses and rob them.

capered (kā′pẽrd): danced about.
capsize (kăp-sīz′): upset.
captive (kăp′tĭv): prisoner.
caravan (kăr′a-văn): a large covered wagon.
caribou (kăr′ĭ-bōō): reindeer.
casements (kās′ments): window-frames.
catalogue (kăt′a-lôg): list of names.
cautiously (kô′shus-ly): carefully.
ceased (sēsd): stopped.
chuckling (chŭk′lĭng): laughing quietly.
cinnamon (sĭn′a-mon): an Asiatic tree, having thick leaves and sweet-smelling bark that is used as a spice.
clambered (klăm′bẽrd): climbed.
cluster (klŭs′tẽr): gather.
clutching (klŭch′ĭng): reaching out to grab.
complained (kom-plānd′): found fault.
concern (kon-sẽrn′): thought.
cote (kōt): a house for doves.

coursers (kôr′sẽrs): swift steeds.
coveted (kŭv′et-ed): longed for.
coyote (kō-yō′tē): prairie wolf.
crags (krăgz): steep, rough rocks.
crones (krōnz): old women.
cupid (kū′pĭd): a beautiful boy, made to look like Cupid, the god of love.
curiosity (kū-rē-ŏs′ĭ-ty): wish to know.
current (kŭr′ent): flow of water.
cypresses (sī′pres-ez): evergreens.

damask (dăm′ask): a figured cloth, first made at Damascus.
delf (dĕlf): a kind of earthenware made at Delft in Holland.
directions (dĭ-rĕk′shonz): ways.
distinct (dĭs-tĭnkt′): marked.
distracted (dĭs-trăk′ted): drawn away.
droll (drōl): funny.
duel (dū′el): a fight between two.

ebony (ĕb′on-y): a hard, black wood.
echoing (ĕk′ō-ĭng): sounding again.
eclipse (e-klĭps′): darkening, hiding by some other heavenly body.
elegant (ĕl′e-gant): graceful.
ember (ĕm′bẽr): burning piece of coal or wood.
embroideries (ĕm-broy′dẽr-ēz): needlework.
enchanted (ĕn-chánt′ed): under the power of magic.
entirely (ĕn-tīr′ly): fully.
errand (ĕr′and): message, business.
escaped (ĕs-kāpd′): got away.
even (ē′ven): evening.
exaggerate (ĕg-ză′jẽr-āt): make too much of.

286

fettle (fĕt'tl): condition.
flutter (flŭt'ēr): in a flutter: worried, upset.
fragrance (frā'grans): sweet smell.
frankincense (frănk'ĭn-sĕns): a sweet-smelling gum from an Arabian tree.
frightened (frī'tend): made afraid.
frowned (frownd): wrinkled the eyebrows in anger.
furbelows (fēr'be-lōz): flounces.

gaudy (gô'dy): brightly coloured.
gentians (jĕn'shanz): a plant that grows in damp places; it has blue or yellow flowers.
gingham (gĭng'am): a cotton cloth woven in stripes or checks.
glowed (glōd): shone brightly.
gnawing (nô'ĭng): biting away at.
gnome (nōm): a fairy dwarf.
goblins (gŏb'linz): mischievous fairies.
gossamer (gŏs'a-mēr): the thin threads like cobwebs, that float about in the air or hang from bushes in fine weather.
guitar (gi-tär'): a stringed instrument, played with the fingers.

haughtily (hô'tĭ-ly): proudly.
haunches (hônsh'ez): hips.
hinder (hĭn'dēr): stop.
hinder (hīn'dēr): back.
holland (hŏl'and): a kind of linen first made in Holland.
hurricane (hŭr'ĭ-kan): a windstorm.

immediately (ĭ-mēd'ē-at-ly): at once.
impatient (ĭm-pā'shent): anxious for a change.
incense (ĭn'sĕns): sweet-smelling spices.
indignant (ĭn-dĭg'nant): angry.
innocence (ĭn'nō-sĕns): a slender plant with small blue flowers.
institute (ĭn'stĭ-tūt): a society formed for a certain purpose.

jessamine (jĕs'a-mĭn): a climbing plant with sweet-smelling white or yellow flowers.
jutting (jŭt'ĭng): sticking out.

kayak (kī'ak): an Eskimo canoe; see page 236.
kirtles (kĕr'tlz): gowns.

lappets (lăp'pets): flaps or folds that make a covering for the ears.
lasso (lăs'ō): a rope with a slip-knot, used for catching animals.
last (låst): a block on which shoes are made.
lattice (lă'tĭs): a network of laths.
legends (lĕ'jendz): stories.
leprosy (lĕp'ro-sy): a skin disease.
littered (lĭt'ērd): filled.
locust (lō'kust): an insect like a grasshopper.
luscious (lŭsh'ŭs): very sweet.
lustre (lŭs'tr): brightness.

macaroons (mă-kă-rōōnz'): little cakes.
manner (măn'ēr): kind.
marigold (măr'ĭ-gōld): a bright orange or yellow flower with a strong perfume.
millet (mĭl'et): a kind of grass seed.
miniature (mĭn'ē-a-tŭr): very small.
mischief (mĭs'chĭf): harm.
motto (mŏt'ō): rule.
multitude (mŭl'tĭ-tūd): great number.
murmured (mēr'mērd): grumbled.
myrrh (mēr): a gum with a bitter taste, used for perfume or incense.

nervous (nēr'vus): easily frightened.
nought (nôt): nothing.

obstacle (ŏb'sta-kl): anything that hinders.
ominous (ŏm'ĭn-us): threatening.
orchids (ôr'kidz): plants with beautiful showy flowers.
oval (ō'val): shaped like an egg.
oyster (oy'stēr): a shell fish.

passenger (păs'en-jēr): traveller.
pasture (păs'tūr): ground covered with grass on which animals feed.
pasty (pås'ty): pie.
peers (pērz): peeps, looks closely.
perish (pĕr'ĭsh): die.

288 A LITTLE DICTIONARY

pickaninny (pĭk'a-nĭn-y): a small Negro child.
pipe (pīp): a long tube of wood or metal on which tunes are played.
pixies (pĭk'sēz): fairies.
plaits (plāts): braids.
primary (prī'ma-ry): first.
prophet (prŏf'et): a person who tells of future happenings.
protect (prō-tĕkt'): keep from harm.
prowled (prowld): wandered about in search of something.
pyramids (pĭr'a-midz): a group of three very large old monuments in Egypt.

quaint (kwānt): unusual, but pretty.
quivers (kwĭ'vẽrz): cases in which arrows are carried.

raging (rāj'ĭng): in great anger.
rebuked (re-būkd'): found fault with.
recognized (rĕk'og-nīzd): knew.
reedy (rē'dy): thin, harsh.
rollicking (rŏl'ĭ-kĭng): playing joyfully.

sage (sāj): wise.
saplings (săp'lĭngz): young trees.
satisfaction (săt-ĭs-făk'shon): pleasure.
savagely (săv'aj-ly): cruelly.
scowls (skowlz): looks angrily.
scramble (skrăm'b'l): climb.
shoon (shōōn): old form of *shoe*.
shutters (shŭt'ẽrz): covers for windows.
slender (slĕn'dẽr): thin.
solitudes (sŏl'ĭtūdz): lonely places.
sovereign (sŏv'ren): above all others, having the highest power.
splinter (splĭn'tẽr): a thin piece.
stalked (stôkd): walked proudly.
startled (stär'tld): frightened.
sullen (sŭl'en): sulky.
surge (sẽrj): wave, flood.
swaddling (swŏd'lĭng): wrapping round like a bandage.

tapestries (tăp'es-trēz): heavy, handwoven coverings for walls and furniture.
tarnished (tär'nĭshd): made dull.
tarried (tă'rēd): waited, delayed.
thatch (thăch): a roof made of rushes.
tidings (tī'dĭngz): news.
token (tō'ken): sign or mark.
traitor (trā'tor): one who is false to a trust.
tramcar (trăm'kär): street-car.
tremendous (tre-mĕn'dus): very large, very great.
tranquil (trăng'kwĭl): quiet, peaceful.
triumph (trī'umf): joy over winning.
tropic (trŏ'pĭk): that part of the earth where the sun seems to turn back on its journey north or south.
trumpeting (trŭm'pet-ĭng): crying loudly.
trundle (trŭn'dl) **bed**: a bed on low wheels.
turban (tẽr'ban): head-dress, cap.
turpentine (tẽr'pen-tīn): an oil obtained from some evergreen trees and used in medicines, paints, etc.

u-miak (ōō'mĭ-ăk): a large Eskimo boat; *see page 239*.
urchins (ẽr'chĭnz): small boys.

vanished (vă'nĭshd): went out of sight.
venture (vĕn'tūr): a dangerous thing done.
violently (vī'o-lĕnt-ly): with great force.
visions (vĭzh'onz): things seen in a dream.
volcano (vŏl-kā'nō): a hill or mountain with an opening at its top, from which are thrown out melted rock, steam, ashes, etc.

wallowed (wäl'ōd): rolled about.

yams (yămz): a kind of sweet potato.